Dr. Lanni's Orgo 1 Lecture Notebook

Laura Lanni, PhD

LMNOPress

Published by LMNO Press, P.O. Box 544, Chapin, SC 29036

ISBN 978-0-9907757-8-2 (pbk.)

A note from the author

Dear Students,

The leap from general chemistry to organic chemistry appears larger than it is. A firm foundation in Lewis structures, VSEPR, shapes of molecules and hybridization, electronegativity trends and bond polarity will help. Basic understanding of acid-base theories, intermolecular forces, and equilibrium will also prove useful. Knowing introductory kinetics and thermodynamics is also useful in making the transition. If you've forgotten these concepts, review them before attempting an organic chemistry course. The gap between your current skills and those needed to succeed in organic chemistry can be bridged by sharpening these general chemistry concepts. Coming to orgo 1 with only hope and determination in your toolbox won't get you far. Such an unstable foundation will quickly crumble.

In organic chemistry you will be required to "see" three-dimensional molecules on a two-dimensional page. If this is difficult for you, a modeling kit will help. Ask your professor (or even better, READ THE SYLLABUS) for advice on good model kits. When you learn about Newman projections, Fischer projections, and cyclohexane chair flips, your modeling kit can save you.

In this first semester of organic chemistry you will build skills to carry you through the second semester. You'll learn stereochemistry, mechanisms, nucleophiles and electrophiles, and organic reactions called substitutions, eliminations, additions, radical reactions, and oxidations.

Organic chemistry lectures may feel like a drawing course. Some students report they spend lecture time writing and drawing furiously and they sacrifice listening to do so. This notebook is a lecture shell for my orgo 1 lectures where students can add notes during lecture and devote more time to listening, discussing, and answering questions. I hope my organization of the topics herein helps my students succeed in mastering the material in orgo 1 so (just in case it isn't your favorite course) you can put this behind you and move on with what *you* love.

To my teaching colleagues: you may use my lecture notes at your own peril for your course, especially when you first start teaching. But your best teaching will come from the natural organization of the course material *in your own way* over many years.

Have a good weekend.

Dr. Lanni

First lecture

COURSE SYLLABUS

    Grading (see syllabus)

    Practice Problems (in textbook(s))

    Calendar (lecture outline, recitation quizzes, exams dates)

Course overview and objectives (topics)

START: Review general chemistry, Preview orgo 1

7

Course calendar on syllabus

Exam dates

Quiz dates

8

A list of prerequisite general chemistry concepts

Prior to your study of organic chemistry, you need a solid foundation in the topics below from your prerequisite general chemistry courses. If you achieved a strong general chemistry comprehension, you can apply that to organic chemistry material. These skills will be briefly reviewed in the first days of the course, in SI or recitation, and subsequently reemphasized and used throughout the two-semester organic chemistry sequence.

- Draw *Lewis dot structures* for a compound or ion given its formula or other representation of the species.
- Use the concept of *electronegativity* to identify *polar and ionic bonds.* Use the concept of electronegativity and knowledge of a compound's *molecular geometry* to assign *partial charges* ($\delta+$ and $\delta-$) and dipole moments.
- A *double bond* is made of a sigma (σ) bond (from direct overlap between sp^2 hybrid orbitals from each atom) and a pi (π) bond (from sideways overlap between unhybridized p orbitals from each atom). A *triple bond* is made of a sigma (σ) bond (between sp hybrid orbitals from each atom) and TWO pi (π) bonds (between TWO PAIRS of unhybridized p orbitals from each atom). There is no free rotation around a double or triple bond due to the sideways overlap of the unhybridized p orbitals in the π bonds. Identify which *intermolecular forces* are present between molecules in a sample (i.e. H-binding, dipole-dipole or London dispersion forces).
- On the basis of the intermolecular forces present, make predictions about properties of a substance like boiling point, melting point or solubility.
- Identify the *hybridization* state of a given atom in a structure and determine the geometry and *bond angles* about the atom.
- Identify electrons in a structure as being in a *sigma* (σ) bond, *pi* (π) bond or nonbonding orbital (*lone pair*).
- Determine the *formal charge* on any atom in a structure or, conversely, given the formal charge on an atom assess how many bonding/nonbonding electrons are present on that atom in a structure.
- Atoms in Lewis structures may *exceed the octet* iff they have an available d sublevel in their outermost principal energy level in the ground state electron configuration. Translation: atoms in Period 2 like carbon, oxygen, and nitrogen with electron configuration ending $2p^x$ do NOT have a 2d sublevel so they cannot exceed the octet.
- Draw *resonance* contributors and the *resonance hybrid* for a given structure.
- Define Arrhenius *acid/base*, Bronsted-Lowry acid/base and Lewis acid/base. Given a structure, determine if it is capable of fulfilling the role of acid or base by one of these definitions.
- Recall *weak acid equilibria*, K_a, and buffered solutions. Given pH, use pK_a to determine whether reactants or products "favored" in a solution.
- Drawing and naming, using IUPAC system, *straight chain and branched alkanes*, up to decane with multiple branches.
- A slow *elementary step* (reaction kinetics) has a high *activation energy*, E_a.
- An *exothermic* reaction releases energy; products have lower energy than reactants. An *endothermic* reaction consumes energy; products have higher energy than reactants.

HOW TO SUCCEED IN ORGANIC CHEMISTRY:
- Build on previous knowledge. Tie new ideas to a solid chemistry understanding. Continually strengthen your knowledge base.
- Read with a **pencil**. Throw away the highlighter. Buy a large eraser.
- Study regularly, daily, all the time. Some students have reported success by studying 10 (or more) hours per week.
- Study should not be just looking over or reading the text or lecture notes. Best "study" for organic requires a **pencil**.
- Review notes following each lecture while consulting textbook for clarification/additional study. Supplement class notes with **additional notes** which YOU take from reading your textbook.
- **Read** ahead. Follow the course calendar and PowerPoint shell and pre-read sections of text before coming to lecture. You will be amazed at how much easier it is to comprehend difficult concepts when you have already exposed your mind to them.
- Do not wait to study until right before the exam. This will be a guaranteed ineffectual method, based on years and years of data provided by former pre-med and pre-pharmacy school students. Short-term memory is insufficient for the depth of understanding required in this course.
- What worked in other courses does NOT work in organic chemistry. For example, memorization is not an effective tool when used alone in a cramming session. Short-term recall capacity is far exceeded by the level of understanding required in organic chemistry.
- Study with a group or partner.
- **Rewrite** the examples from lecture until you completely understand them.
- Do not fall behind. Build a solid foundation or your organic tower might crumble like a stack of cards in the wind.
- Ask questions in lecture.
- If you need a private tutor, get one right away. (The chemistry department has a list of private tutors for organic chemistry.)
- Bring specific questions to office hours which demonstrate the hours of effort you have already put into the material.
- Prioritize your academic life. And put this course very close to the top of your list.

Introduction to organic chemistry

11

Organic Chemistry

Organic chemistry: study of compounds containing the element carbon.

Examples: propane, acetic acid, acetone, acetylene, polyester, octane, methane, ethanol, nylon, Kevlar, polyethylene terephthalate, 3,3-diethyl-2,5,6-trimethylheptane, naphthalene, toluene...

12

General chemistry review for you:

Complete this chart using your general chemistry knowledge/notes on VSEPR **before the first lecture.**

Always read the fine print.

# electron domains on central atom (# effective electron pairs)	electron geometry around central atom	hybridization of central atom	example
2			
3			
4			
5			
6			

13

General chemistry review

Draw the Lewis structure of **water**.

How many **valence electrons** are in the molecule?
How many **effective electron pairs** on the central atom?
How many **lone pairs of electrons** on the central atom?
How many **bonding pairs of electrons** are on the central atom?
What is the **electron geometry** around the central atom?
What is the **molecular geometry (shape)** of the molecule?
What is the **hybridization** of the central atom?
How many **sigma (σ) bonds** in the molecule?
How many **pi (π) bonds** in the molecule?
Are there **polar bonds** in the molecule?
Is the **molecule polar**?

14

General chemistry PRACTICE—you try one

Draw the Lewis structure of **ammonia (NH_3)**.

How many valence electrons are in the molecule?
How many effective electron pairs on the central atom?
How many lone pairs of electrons on the central atom?
How many bonding pairs of electrons are on the central atom?
What is the electron geometry around the central atom?
What is the molecular geometry (shape) of the molecule?
What is the hybridization of the central atom?
How many sigma (σ) bonds in the molecule?
How many pi (π) bonds in the molecule?
Are there polar bonds in the molecule?
Is the molecule polar?

General chemistry more PRACTICE for you after lecture

Draw the Lewis structure of
formaldehyde (H_2CO)

carbon dioxide (CO_2)

ethane (C_2H_6)

ethene (C_2H_4)

ethyne (C_2H_2)

acetic acid (CH_3COOH)
(many "central atoms" so analyze every non-hydrogen atom)

More practice: scan your textbook or this document and draw
the Lewis structure of any molecule or ion you find.

For each, also answer these questions:

How many valence electrons are in the molecule?
How many effective electron pairs on the central atom?
How many lone pairs of electrons on the central atom?
How many bonding pairs of electrons are on the central atom?
What is the electron geometry around the central atom?
What is the molecular geometry (shape) of the molecule?
What is the hybridization of the central atom?
How many sigma (σ) bonds in the molecule?
How many pi (π) bonds in the molecule?
Are there polar bonds in the molecule?
Is the molecule polar?

More review and some NEW material: a list

Review: how to use general chemistry skills to transition to organic chemistry?

  Formal charge (general chemistry *review*)

  Resonance (general chemistry *review*)

  Shapes of simple organic molecules (*maybe* general chemistry review)

NEW: how do organic chemists draw molecules?

  Structural formulas of organic molecules

  Leaving off the hydrogens

  Leaving off the carbons (skeletal/line structures)

  Leaving off the lone pairs when we know they are there.

  Counting atoms (C, H, O, etc) in line structures

17

Review Formal charge

Formal charge = #VE - #bonds - # lone electrons

#VE = **valence electrons** *on the atom under consideration*

#**bonds** *on the atom under consideration*: single = 1, double counts as 2, triple counts as 3

#**lone electrons**: unshared electrons *on the atom under consideration*. Count the dots.

18

Formal charge examples

Examples: water, hydroxide, hydronium, ammonia, ammonium, formaldehyde, ozone, more?

Review Resonance

Resonance: when more than one Lewis structure can be written for a molecule WITHOUT CHANGING THE CONNECTIVITY of any atoms—ONLY moving electrons (usually in pairs), there are multiple resonance structures.
We say the molecule 'has resonance.'
The multiple structures are called 'resonance structures'
A molecule (or ion) is a combination (average/hybrid) which encompasses every possible resonance structure.

Do not exceed the octet (8 electrons) on any Period 2 element (C, N, O, etc.)
    8 electrons = 4 bonds
        Or 3 bonds and 1 lone pair
        Or 2 bonds and 2 lone pairs
        Or 1 bond   and 3 lone pairs
(But in a cation, an atom *may have less* than 8 electrons)

Examples: ozone, acetate, benzene, more (on next slide)

Resonance

(the true structure is not adequately represented by a single Lewis structure)

Examples

Do not exceed the octet (8 electrons) on any period 2 element (C, N, O, etc)

8 electrons = 4 bonds

Or 3 bonds and 1 lone pair

Or 2 bonds and 2 lone pairs

Or 1 bond and 3 lone pairs   21

(But in a cation, an atom *may have less* than 8 electrons)

Resonance

(the true structure is not adequately represented by a single Lewis structure)

When an ion has resonance structures, it is "resonance stabilized" because the *charge is delocalized* across more than one atom.

Be careful when drawing resonance structures to avoid these common student errors.

*Don't move atoms.

*Move "loose electrons" like lone pairs and pi bonds.

*Don't move electrons to an sp^3 atom that already has an octet (8 electrons). To avoid this you must know where the hydrogens are. Draw them on if it helps you.

22

REVIEW: Covalent bond formation (by looking at carbon to carbon bonds)

Single, double and triple carbon to carbon bonds

ethane   ethene   ethyne

23

How to *describe* other covalent bonds (using hybrid or atomic orbitals, so this leans on general chemistry skills again)

Water, ammonia, formaldehyde, more?

24

Drawing organic structures
(guidelines)

Drawing organic structures
(guidelines)

Carbons, hydrogens, and lone e⁻ pairs are implied/understood (not shown). But always include non-zero formal charges.

Do not exceed an octet on C, O, N

In organic molecules:

neutral carbon makes __ bonds (example: methane)

neutral nitrogen makes __ bonds (example: ammonia)

neutral oxygen makes __ bonds (example: water)

Drawing organic structures (examples)

Examples: diethyl ether, dimethyl ether, ethanol

Drawing organic structures

[More examples with carbons, hydrogens, lone pairs implied/understood (not shown).]

More examples: propane, acetic acid, 2-methylpentane

Drawing organic structures (count up the hydrogens)
More examples: What is the formula for each?

Resonance practice/review

Draw all resonance structures of

Laura Lanni   15

Radicals, cations, anions (on carbons)

Examples:

Methyl radical   **methyl cation**   **methyl anion**

Preview of organic functional groups

Alcohol

Ether

carboxylic acid

Ester

Ketone

Aldehyde

alkyl halide

Amide

amine

Functional group PRACTICE

Identify all the functional groups in prostaglandin E_1 (hormone)

Also add all lone pairs of electrons.

More practice for you: Resonance again

Draw valid resonance structure for each carbocation.

Be careful.
Consider formal charges, hybridization of non-hydrogen atoms.
Must think about where the lone pairs of electrons and hydrogens are by using formal charge formula and given charges.

Bond-line structures in 3-D

All molecules take up space in 3 dimensions. It is difficult to represent them on a 2D paper.

We use dashes (aka hashes) or solid wedges to show groups or atoms that point back away from you into the paper or toward you out of the paper

35

Resonance recap

Resonance pattern examples

| one curved arrow lone pair adjacent to carbocation | one curved arrow π bond to lone pair | one curved arrow π bond to allylic carbocation | two curved arrows lone pair to π bond and π bond to atom | three curved arrows conjugated π bonds |

36

More examples and practice for you (a great page for an SI session)

1. Add all lone pairs to this ion,

$$\overset{\ominus}{O}-N=O$$

2. Draw the skeletal structure of $CH_3CH_2CH(CH_2CH_3)CH_2COOH$

3. Draw the skeletal structure of $CH_3C(CH_3)_2CH_3$

4a. What is the formula for 2-methylpropanoic acid (shown)?

4b. Add all lone pairs of electrons to the structure.

Refer to this carbocation for questions 5-9.

$$H-\overset{\oplus}{\underset{\underset{H}{|}}{C}}-\overset{O}{\underset{}{}}-H$$

5a. Use the Periodic Table to sum the valence electrons in this ion. Total VE = _____

5b. Add lone pairs of electrons to atoms in the ion as appropriate and verify use of the correct number of total valence electrons.

6. Draw an alternative Lewis structure (a resonance structure) for this ion.

7. What is the shape around the carbon?

8. What is the shape around the oxygen?

9. Describe the C-O bond.

Organic Acids and Bases

Organic Acids and Bases (again, depend upon and build on your general chemistry knowledge)

More general chemistry **review**
    acids and bases
    Bronsted-Lowry and Lewis definitions
    conjugate acid-base pairs
    equilibrium
    K_a (acid dissociation constant)
    pH (scale, relationship to hydrogen ion concentration)

New
    pK_a (refer to the p in pH for a clue)
    effect of structure on acid strength
    effect of conjugate base stabilization on acid strength
    acids protonated or not based on pH (Henderson-Hasselbalch/general chemistry)
    Mechanism of acid base reaction (protonate/deprotonate)

39

Review: Acids and bases (Bronsted Lowry / Conjugate acid-base pairs)

Bronsted Lowry acid: *loses* a proton (H^+)

Bronsted Lowry base: *gains* a proton (H^+)

Think about it: Does the acid "give" the proton or does the base "take it"? Where do the electrons in the new bond come from?

Examples

40

Review: Acids and bases (Lewis theory)

Lewis acid: electron pair acceptor (electrophilic)

Lewis base: electron pair donor (nucleophilic)

Examples

pH, K_a

Recall from general chemistry: $pH = -\log[H^+]$

Low pH, indicates a more acidic solution because more ionized H^+ results in higher concentration of hydronium $[H_3O^+]$ at equilibrium in aqueous solution)

Examples and discussion

Laura Lanni

pK_a

Lower pK_a indicates stronger acid

$pK_a = -\log[K_a]$

Can use pK_as to predict the equilibrium position in an acid-base reaction

Examples and discussion

Structure and acid strength: examples

Recall from general chemistry: The weaker the base, the stronger the conjugate acid.

Organic perspective: the *more stable* the base (*less reactive/weaker*), the stronger its conjugate acid.

Structural factors and examples to consider:
electronegativity
hybridization
size
substituent effect
resonance

Structure and acid strength: examples

Electronegativity affects base stability (and conjugate acid strength)

Compare acidity of molecules with central atom from **same Period** (use electronegativity trend).
Example CH_4, NH_3, H_2O, HF

Structure and acid strength: examples

Hybridization of atom affects acidity of proton on it.
Example: compare C_2H_2, C_2H_4, C_2H_6

Structure and acid strength: examples

Size: for comparison of acids with central atom in *same Group (family, column)*, size matters
Example: HF, HCl, HBr, HI

Structure and acid strength: examples

substituent effect on acid strength—inductive effect
Example: compare acetic acid, iodoacetic acid, bromoacetic acid, chloroacetic acid, fluoroacetic acid

Structure and acid strength: examples

Resonance is a stabilizing effect. (A more stable base is a weaker base and has a stronger conjugate acid)

Example: Compare acetic acid to ethanol

Tie structure analysis back to pK_a

pK_a = -log K_a
(Reminder: Lower pK_a means stronger acid)

some pK_as to know

(When asked to compare acidity of two protons (ionizable hydrogens) on two molecules, the "stronger acid" or "more stable conjugate base" (see examples) will be based on structure analysis. However, knowing some pK_a values is a quick way to check.)

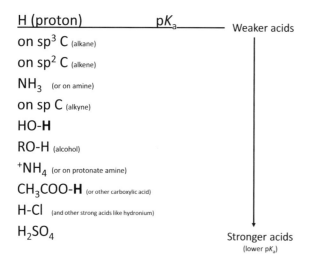

H (proton)	pK_a	
on sp^3 C (alkane)		Weaker acids
on sp^2 C (alkene)		
NH$_3$ (or on amine)		
on sp C (alkyne)		
HO-**H**		
RO-H (alcohol)		
$^+$NH$_4$ (or on protonate amine)		
CH$_3$COO-**H** (or other carboxylic acid)		
H-Cl (and other strong acids like hydronium)		
H$_2$SO$_4$		Stronger acids (lower pK_a)

51

pH effect on structure of an organic compound

The question: Will it be protonated or not?

 Will the species in equilibrium with its conjugate (acid or base) exist predominantly

 (in higher concentration) in the acid or conjugate base form?

The answer: Based on analysis of the Henderson-Hasselbalch equation:

If **pH solution < pK_a**, the molecule will exist mostly in its acidic (protonated, conjugate acid) form (HA)

If **pH solution > pKa**, the molecule will exist in mostly its basic (deprotonated, conjugate base) form (A$^-$)

52

Examples: what is the major species at equilibrium in an aqueous solution at a specific pH?

An aqueous solution of ethanol (pK_a 16) has a pH of 5.
(Therefore, ethanol (solute) is predominantly **protonated**.)

An aqueous solution of acetic acid has pH of 9.
(Therefore, solute (acetic acid) exists predominantly as **acetate**.)

53

Acid base reactions/equilibria: MECHANISM
Before class, write the balanced reaction for each example.

Example:
Hydronium and ammonia react to make water and ammonium

Another:
Acetic acid and hydroxide react to make acetate and water

54

Practice

How many hydrogens are on this molecule?

A. 14
B. 15
C. 16
D. 17
E. 18
F. 19
G. 20
H. 21

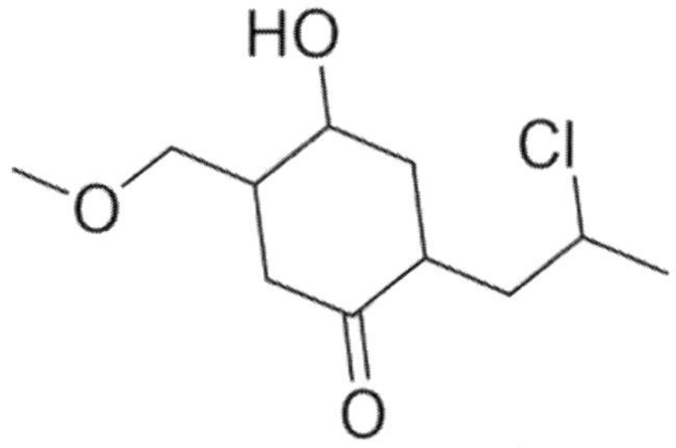

Practice

How many of these will exist predominantly in the protonated state at a pH of 10?

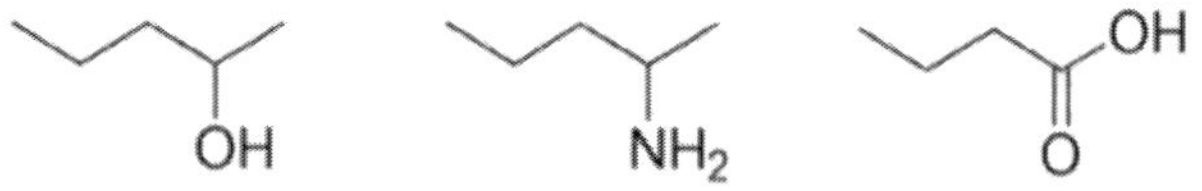

A. 0
B. 1
C. 2
D. 3

Practice: Functional groups again

Identify the following functional groups in a chemical structure: alkane, alkene, alkyne, **arene** (aromatic), amine, alcohol, ether, alkyl halide, aldehyde, ketone, carboxylic acid, ester, **acid chloride** and **amide**.

57

Alkanes and cycloalkanes: a topic list as we start looking at organic molecules

Alkanes
Constitutional isomers
Branched alkanes
Cycloalkanes
Alcohols
Alkyl halides
IUPAC nomenclature
conformational analysis
Newman projections
cyclohexane analysis

See the course syllabus for a suggested molecular modeling kit to help you visualize three-dimensional molecules.

58

Alkanes and cycloalkanes

General Chemistry Review Alkanes

All (neutral) carbons make four (4) covalent bonds
All carbon-carbon bonds in alkanes are single bonds
All carbons in alkanes are tetrahedral
All carbons in alkanes are sp^3 hybridized
Alkane general formula C_nH_{2n+2}

IUPAC names of simple alkanes

Use prefixes corresponding to # of carbons:

meth	eth	prop	but	pent	hex	hept	oct	non	dec
1	2	3	4	5	6	7	8	9	10

Laura Lanni

Constitutional isomers

Have the same chemical formula, but different molecular structure (different connectivity of atoms)

Examples

1. Ethanol and dimethyl ether (C_2H_6O)

2. Pentane and 2-methylbutane (C_5H_{12})

3. Chloropropanes, C_3H_7Cl, draw them to show many isomers are possible.

4. How about the dichloropropanes ($C_3H_5Cl_2$)?

61

Naming branched alkanes

use IUPAC nomenclature, and consider constitutional isomers

Find and name **longest carbon chain**

Number the carbons in the chain to give the substituent (branch) the lowest possible number

Name the **branches** alphabetically, each preceded by its number indicating its position

Use **prefixes** di- tri- tetra- etc to denote more than one of a given type of substituent

Numbers–letters must be separated by **dash**

Numbers, numbers must be separated by **comma**

Put it all together: branches 1st, longest chain last

(That's a long list. Examples should help. But first, a list of carbon substitutents..)

62

Alkyl branch names ("substituents")

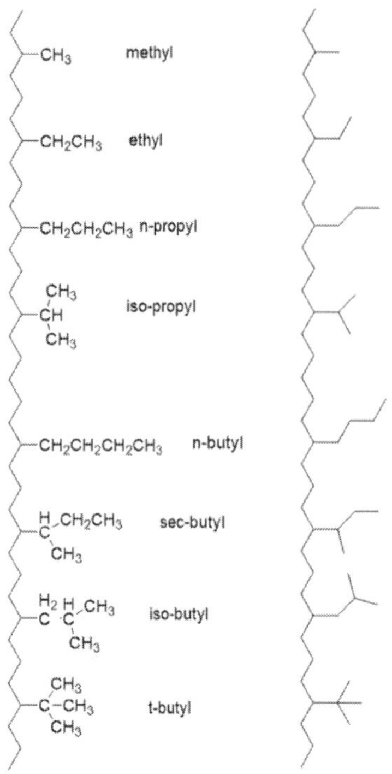

- -CH$_3$ methyl
- -CH$_2$CH$_3$ ethyl
- -CH$_2$CH$_2$CH$_3$ n-propyl
- iso-propyl   aka 1-methylethyl
- -CH$_2$CH$_2$CH$_2$CH$_3$ n-butyl
- sec-butyl   aka 1-methylpropyl
- iso-butyl   aka 2-methylpropyl
- t-butyl   aka 2,2-dimethylethyl

63

Examples of branched alkanes and naming them

64

Examples of branched alkanes and naming them and now add… considering constitutional isomers

Practice

Try these. Give IUPAC name of each.

Be able to write the formula for each hydrocarbon, indicate hybridization of each carbon, pK_a of the hydrogens, shape around each carbon.

Cycloalkanes, structures and nomenclature

Formula C_nH_{2n}

Name "cyclo...."

(*cis*, *trans* sterochem) (later)

examples

Extra practice to add to your homework

Draw and name all cycloalkane constitutional isomers of C_6H_{12}.

Naming alkyl halides (R-X, where X is a halogen)

Branch names have -o suffix:

    F   fluoro

    Cl   chloro

    Br   bromo

    I   iodo

Examples: 2-chloroheptane

2,3-dibromopentane

69

Naming alkyl halides (RX, where X is a halogen)

More examples

1-chloro-3-methylheptane

1-bromo-3-iodocyclohexane
(there are *cis* and *trans* isomers—but
wedges and dashes were not indicated
so we'll get to that later)

Try one backwards: draw 1,2-dibromo-2,4,4-trimethylhexane (and then write its formula)

70

Naming alcohols (ROH)

Number to indicate which carbon is bonded to the oxygen of the alcohol group
Add suffix –ol

Examples:

1-propanol

2-propanol (aka iso-propanol)

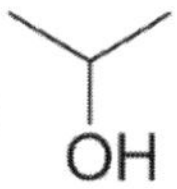

ethanol

2-methyl-2-pentanol

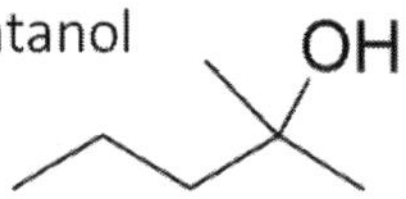

71

Naming alcohols

Examples

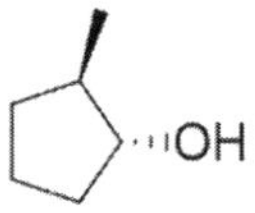

trans-2-methylcyclopentanol

3-fluoro-1-propanol

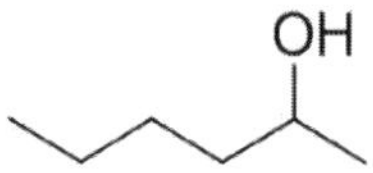

2-hexanol

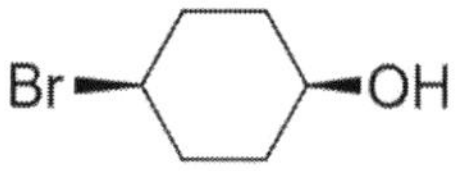

cis-4-bromocyclohexanol

72

Laura Lanni

36

Primary (1°), secondary (2°) and tertiary (3°) compounds (RX and ROH)

Primary alcohol

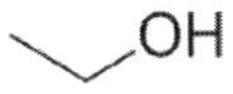

Primary alkyl halide

Secondary alcohol

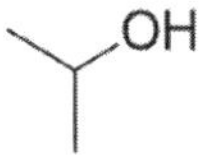

Secondary alkyl halide

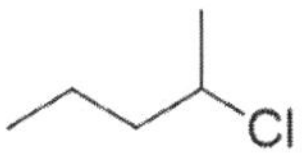

Tertiary alcohol

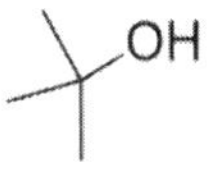

Tertiary alkyl halide

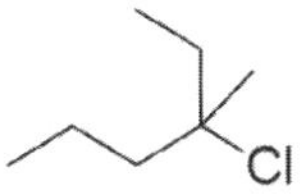

73

Primary (1°), secondary (2°) and tertiary (3°) compounds (RX and ROH)

Pattern

On carbon where OH or X is bonded, there are

#H	designation	(#R groups)
2	1° (primary)	(1)
1	2° (secondary)	(2)
0	3° (tertiary)	(3)

(R = alkyl group)

74

Intermolecular forces in **hydrocarbons** (alkanes and cycloalkanes)
(and alkenes, and alkynes, and aromatics)

In HYDROCARBONS

Hydrogen bonding? NO
Dipole-dipole? NO (non-polar molecules)
London dispersion forces (aka induced dipoles, aka LDF)? YES

Alkane Properties are based on strength of LDFs
Example: Stronger LDF→ higher boiling point

75

(general chemistry review)
Hydrocarbon property trends

Branched alkanes have LOWER boiling points than their unbranched isomers
(example)

Longer alkanes have higher boiling points than shorter alkanes
(example)

76

(Review from general chemistry)
Hydrocarbon solubility

Hydrocarbons (alkanes, etc) are insoluble in water

WHY?

Boiling points and intermolecular forces (IMFs) in RX and ROH

Due to polar bonds in the molecules, both alkyl halides (RX) and alcohols (ROH) are **polar molecules.**
Therefore, there are dipole-dipole forces between the molecules in pure samples of both RX and ROH.
And there are hydrogen bonds between the molecules in pure samples of ROH.

Boiling points and IMFs in alcohols ROH

Example: ethanol

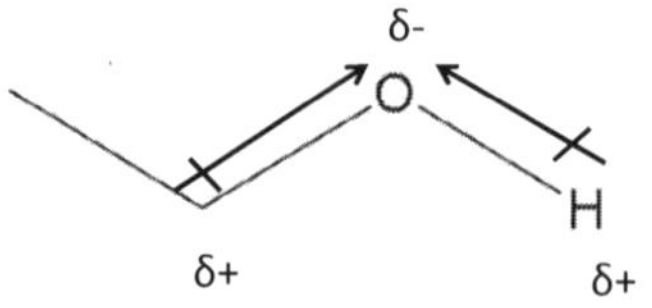

$\delta-$
$\delta+$ $\delta+$

IMF: dipole-dipole and **hydrogen bonding** (strongest IMF)

High boiling points

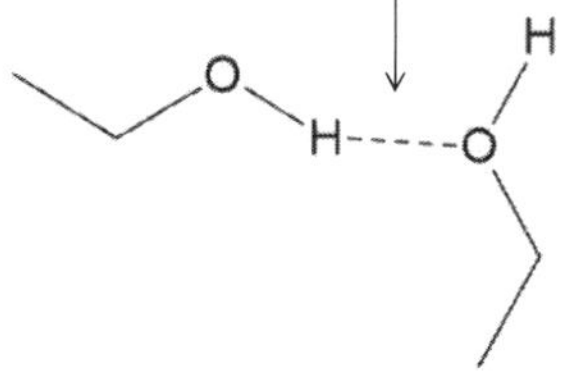

79

Boiling points and IMFs in alkyl halides RX

Example: 1-chloropropane

IMF: dipole-dipole

Higher boiling point with larger X (more polarizable—easier to distort electron cloud)

80

Conformational analysis

Conformational analysis

3-dimensional representations of alkanes and cycloalkanes
like Newman projections and cyclohexane conformations
are very challenging to visualize (for beginners) without a model kit.

Use a model kit to help you SEE the molecules. (See model kit suggested in course syllabus.)

Free rotation around sigma (σ) bonds

Due to free rotation around σ bonds, alkanes and cycloalkanes exist in multiple **conformations**. (Use model kit to see this.)

FREE ROTATION AROUND SIGMA BONDS Newman projections

Conformational analysis and Newman Projections

Analysis of stability of different conformations

Terms: staggered, eclipsed, gauche, antiperiplanar, dihedral angle.

Free rotation around σ bonds

Some CONFORMATIONS of **butane** C_4H_{10}

Free rotation around σ bonds

Ethane C_2H_6

Staggered conformation   Eclipsed conformation

These interconvert rapidly at room temperature by rotation around the C1-C2 bond.
Build with model kit and rotate to view each conformation.

Newman projections of ethane

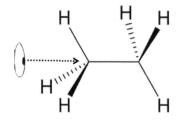

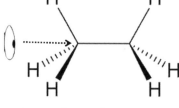

Staggered conformation   Eclipsed conformation

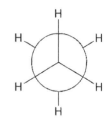

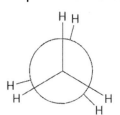

87

Newman projections of ethane

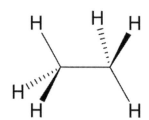

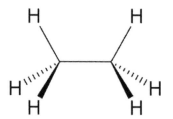

Staggered: more stable by __ kcal/mol than eclipsed

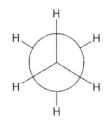

88

Newman projection:
names of relative positions

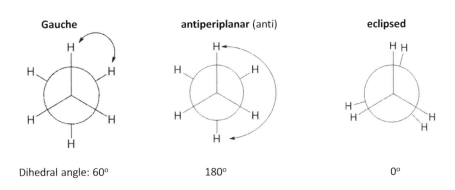

Gauche	antiperiplanar (anti)	eclipsed
Dihedral angle: 60°	180°	0°

Dihedral angle: angle between two intersecting planes—
    through 2 sets of 3 atoms having 2 atoms in common.

89

Potential energy diagram for ethane

Remember, staggered conformation is more stable by ~3 kcal/mol than eclipsed.
Eclipsed is less stable (most torsional strain)

90

Butane again

Which are staggered?
Which are eclipsed?

Potential energy diagram for butane (sighted along the C_2-C_3 bond)

Application of Newman projection: Name this structure

More Newman Practice

You try these later (for homework / at SI / in office hours)

1. Draw all conformations (360° analysis) and energy diagram for butane sighted along the C_1-C_2 bond.

2. Draw each Newman projection along the indicated bond and name each molecule.

Practice

What is the correct order of stability (from most to least stable) of the Newman projections of butane?

1. (Me-Me antiperiplanar)   2. (Me-Me gauche)   3. (Me-Me eclipsed)   4. (Me-H eclipsed)

A) 1, 2, 3, 4
B) 4, 3, 2, 1
C) 1, 4, 2, 3
D) 3, 2, 4, 1
E) None of these are correct.

95

Practice

Which of the following schemes represent the correct movement of electrons and resonance structures?

A. [structure] ⟷ [structure]

C. [structure] ⟷ [structure]

B. [structure] ⟷ [structure]

D. [structure] ⟷ [structure]

96

Cycloalkanes again

97

Cycloalkanes review and details

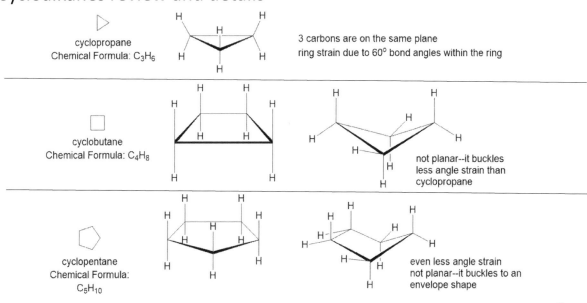

cyclopropane
Chemical Formula: C_3H_6

3 carbons are on the same plane
ring strain due to 60° bond angles within the ring

cyclobutane
Chemical Formula: C_4H_8

not planar--it buckles
less angle strain than
cyclopropane

cyclopentane
Chemical Formula:
C_5H_{10}

even less angle strain
not planar--it buckles to an
envelope shape

98

Focus on cyclohexane

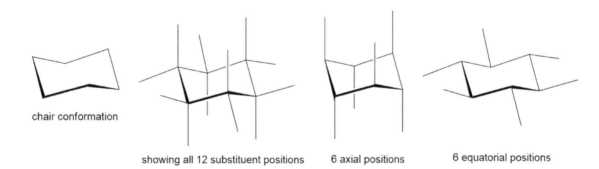

cyclohexane
Chemical Formula:
C_6H_{12}

Chair

Boat

99

Cyclohexane **chair** conformation: axial and equatorial positions on carbons in the ring

chair conformation

showing all 12 substituent positions

6 axial positions

6 equatorial positions

100

Laura Lanni

50

Practice

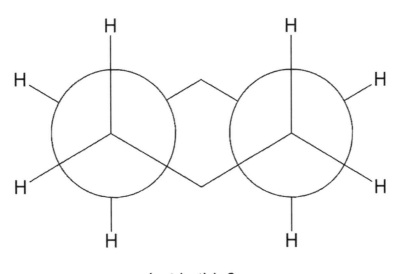

what is this?

Cyclohexane chair flip

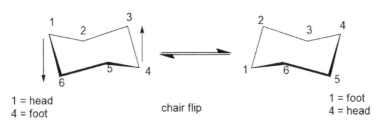

1 = head
4 = foot

chair flip

1 = foot
4 = head

When chair is flipped, axial positions become equatorial and vice versa-build with your kit and look at model to confirm.

Another Mystery Newman Projection

what is this?

Practice: constitutional isomer example

Be able to draw and name all isomers that may be named #,#-**dimethylcyclohexane**.
How many are there?

Visualize dimethylcyclohexane isomers: 1,1 / 1,2 / 1,3 / 1,4-dimethylcyclohexanes

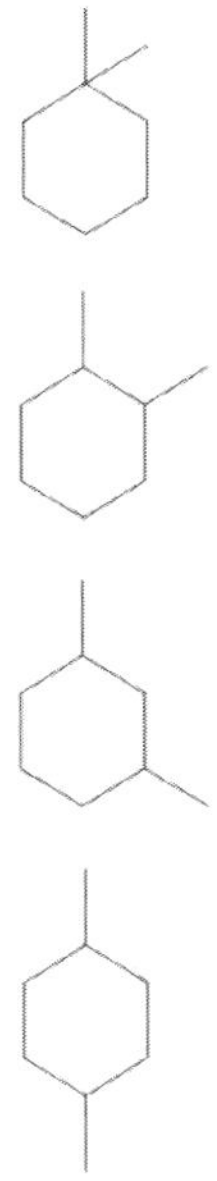

105

3-dimensional visualization practice: Are any of these diethylcyclohexane structures equivalent?

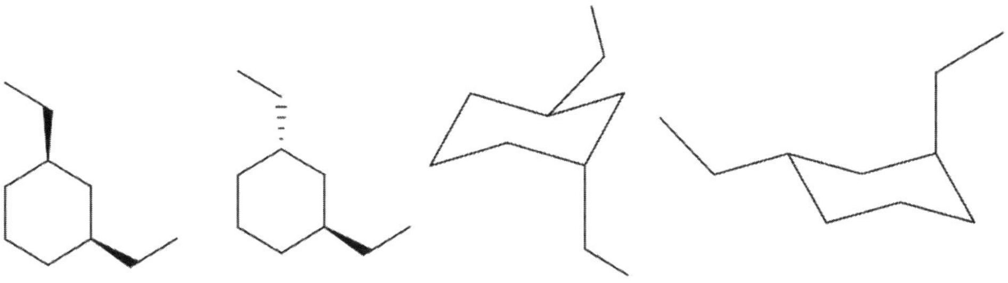

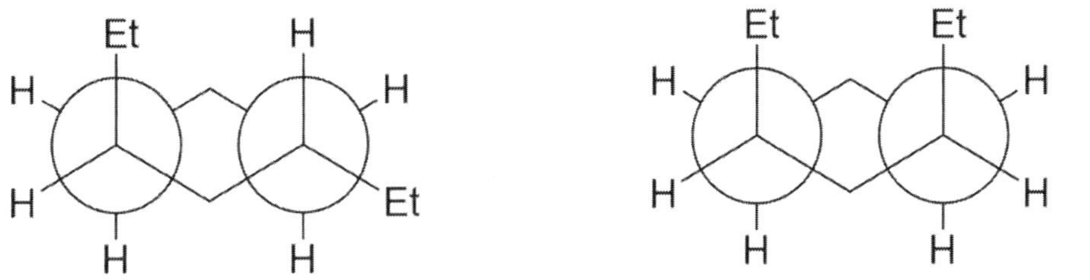

106

di-, tri- and more substituted cyclohexanes

cis and trans branches
How to draw the chair depiction given the wedge-dash depiction
Why are wedges and dashes NOT OK on the chair depiction of cyclohexane?
Many examples...

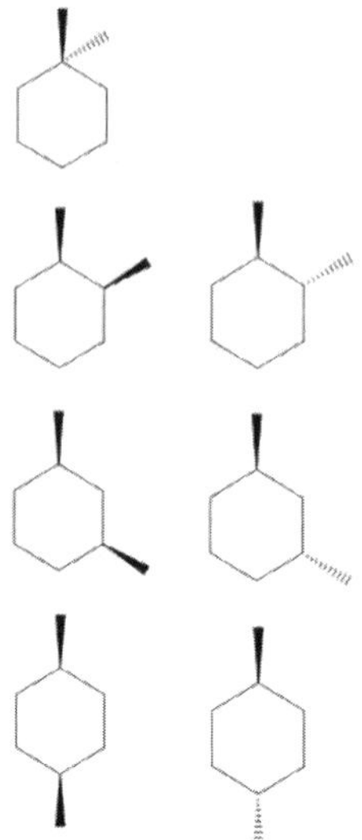

107

di-, tri- and more substituted cyclohexanes
examples

108

Pattern from examples—orientation analysis of any two substituents on cyclohexane

	cis	*trans*
1,2		
1,3		
1,4		

Polycyclic molecules

Example: **decalin**

Formula?

2 structural isomers:

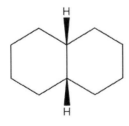

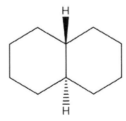

cis-decalin   trans-decalin

Laura Lanni

cis and *trans* decalin depicted in chair conformations

Which is which?

Cholesterol

Carbon shell showing cycloalkanes

...with 2 methyls, alcohol, 3 significant protons added

Laura Lanni

56

More practice with substituted cyclohexanes

More practice with substituted cyclohexanes

MORE PRACTICE FOR YOU

1. How many carbons are on the molecule?
2. How many hydrogens are on the molecule?
3. How many sigma (σ) bonds?
4. How many pi (π) bonds?
5. How many carbons are sp^2 hybridized?
6. How many tetrahedral carbons are there?
7. What is the shape around every oxygen that is covalently bonded to a hydrogen?
8. What are all of the bond angles (in degrees) around the carbons in the 6-membered rings?
9. How many cyclohexane units are there?
10. Which of the indicated hydrogens is the most acidic proton?
11. What is the approximate pK_a of the most acidic proton?
12. At pH =7, will the most acidic proton remain on the molecule, or will the molecule exist predominantly in the deprotonated form at that site?
13. What functional groups are on this molecule?
14. In the molecular formula $C_v N_w O_x H_y F_z$, what are the values of v, w, x, y, and z, respectively?

115

1. What is the formula?
2. How many σ and π bonds?
3. What is the hybridization of every non-H atom?
4. What are all of the bond angles and shapes around each atom?
5. What is the most acidic proton and what is its approximate pK_a?

116

Laura Lanni

58

Newman practice

Use a model kit to help with this one.

Draw a Newman projection along the *C1-C2* bond in *cis*-1,2-dimethylcyclohexane, including both chairs and a boat conformation.

Examine the diaxial, eclipsed interactions in the boat conformation, and the gauche interactions in the chair conformations. (The Newman projections and the model kit together can help you visualize axial and equatorial groups.)

Is there any reason to think one of the chair conformations is more stable than the other?

117

STEREOCHEMISTRY

118

Stereochemistry topic list

(another chapter where your model kit may help you visualize 3-dimensional molecules)

Molecular chirality

Chiral center (stereogenic center)

Symmetry, optical activity

Configurations

Cahn-Ingold-Prelog system for determining absolute configuration (R and S designations)

Molecules with multiple chiral centers

Enantiomers and diastereomers

Meso compounds

Enantiomeric excess

119

Introductory definitions

Stereochemistry: chemistry in 3 dimensions

Isomers with the same connectivity but different spatial arrangement of their atoms are **stereoisomers**.

Chiral: describes an object which is not superimposable on its mirror image. (Ex: your hands)

Achiral: not chiral.

120

Examples of stereoisomerism in chiral molecules you might have already noticed (or will see soon)

cis and *trans* branches on **cycloalkanes**

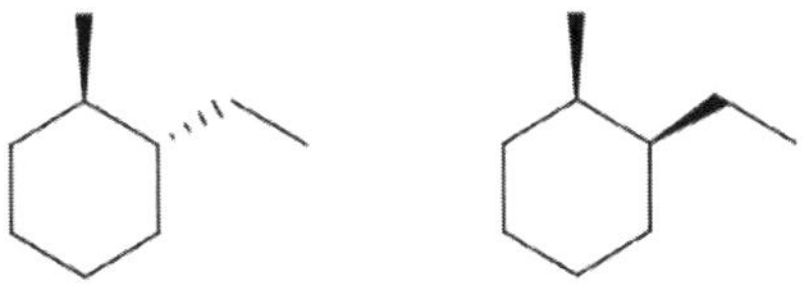

cis and *trans* stereoisomers of **alkenes**

Focus of our study: chirality of sp^3 tetrahedral centers

Example: 2-bromobutane

These molecules are mirror images which are not superimposable on each other

ENANTIOMERS

Build them with your model kit.

Achiral

A molecule which IS superimposable on its mirror image

Example: 2-bromopropane

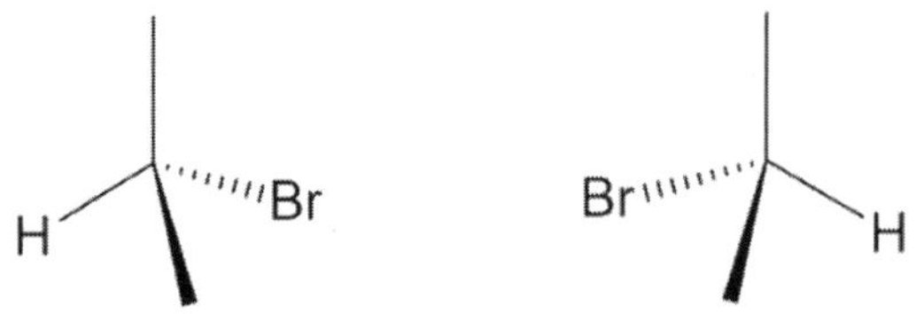

Build each with your model kit.
[   ] mirror image is the same molecule (superimposable)

123

Achiral

Achiral molecules have a plane of symmetry—an internal mirror plane that reflects half the molecule back on itself

Examples

Build 3-bromopentane and 2-bromo-2-methylbutane and examine their internal mirror planes

124

Chiral center

Also called a stereogenic center: a tetrahedral (sp³) carbon with **four *different* atoms or groups** bonded to it.

Example: 2-bromobutane

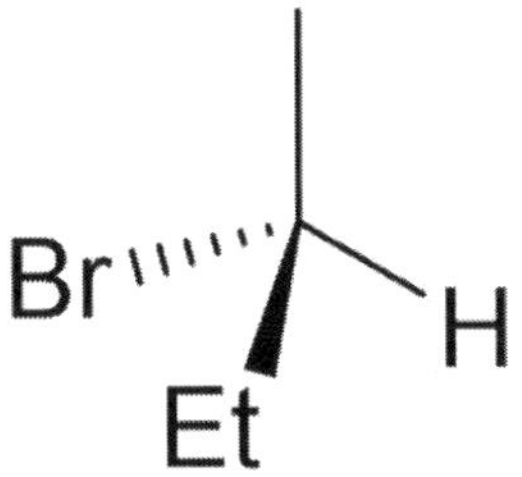

Carbon number 2 is a chiral center because it is bonded to
a hydrogen, a methyl, an ethyl, and a bromide

125

Practice: Mark Chiral centers with asterisk*

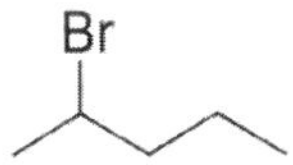

2-bromopentane

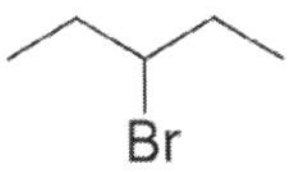

3-bromopentane

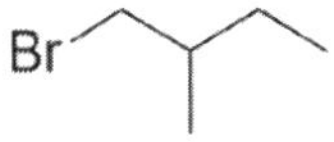

1-bromo-2-methylbutane

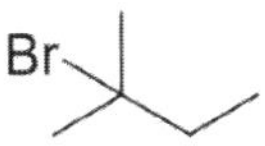

2-bromo-2-methylbutane

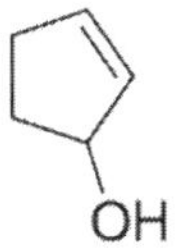

3-cyclopentenol

126

Assigning absolute configuration to each chiral center (R, S)

Use Cahn-Ingold-Prelog system to rank groups on chiral carbon
from highest priority (1) to lowest (4) priority

Highest priority atom has highest atomic number—give it CIP "1"
Lowest priority atom has lowest atomic number—give it CIP "4"
Break ties by going to the next bonded atom(s) and applying CIP to them.

Examples to practice CIP ranking

Assigning absolute configuration to each chiral center (R, S)

✓ Use Cahn-Ingold-Prelog system to rank groups on chiral carbon from lowest (4) to highest
  priority (1)

THEN...

➤ Point the 4th group **away**

➤ Count 1,2,3 in a circle

R = 1,2,3 clockwise   S = 1,2,3 counterclockwise

clockwise   counterclockwise
R   S

Example (R, S) "absolute configuration"

Is this chiral center R or S?

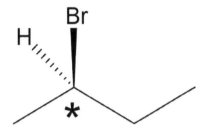

Practice (R, S)

Label every chiral center as R or S

Me
|
HO———H
|
Et

OH
|
Me———H
Et

Practice (R, S)

Label every chiral center as R or S
(2 chiral centers!!)

Practice (R, S)

Label every chiral center as R or S

Laura Lanni

Practice (R, S)

Label every chiral center as R or S

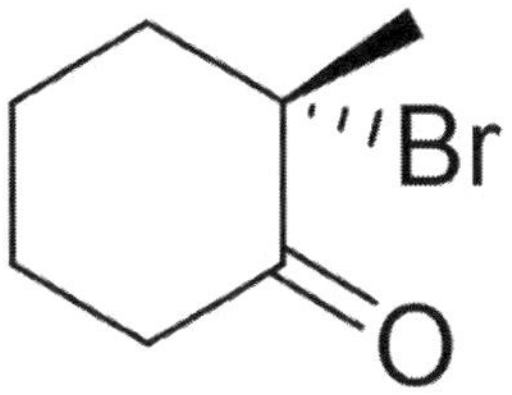

enantiomer

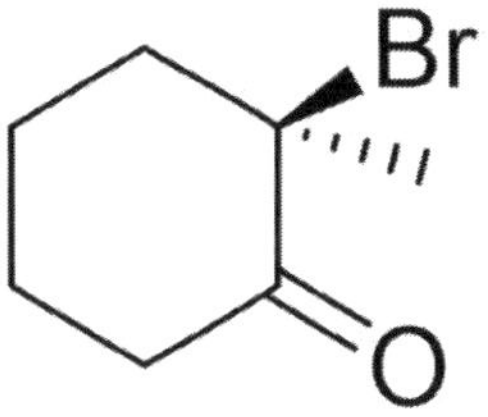

133

Practice (R, S)

Label every chiral center as R or S

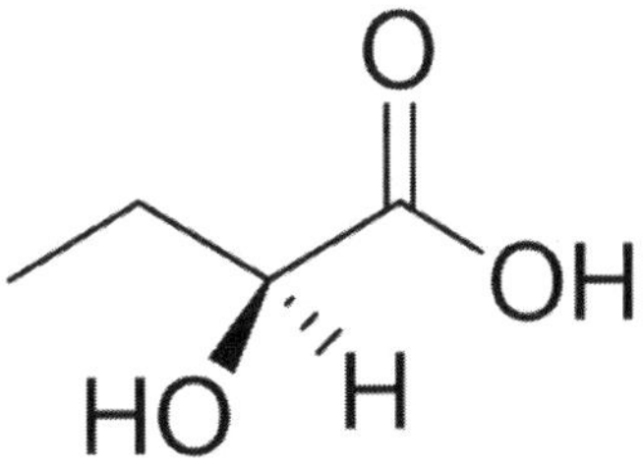

134

Practice (R, S)

Label every chiral center as R or S

enantiomer

Absolute configuration—more examples for practice

HOW MANY CHIRAL CENTERS?

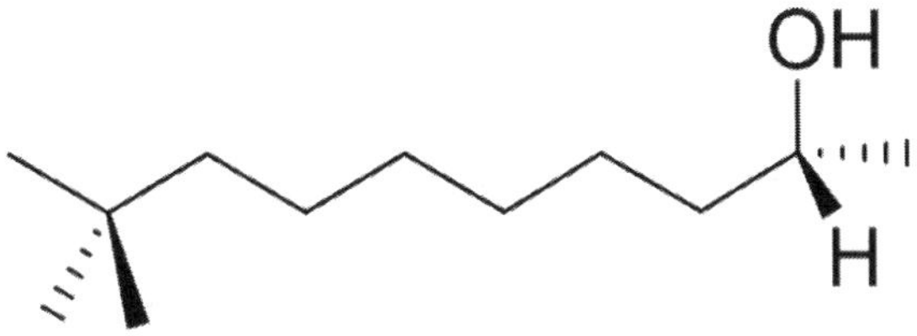

137

Enantiomers

Nonsuperimposable mirror images

To draw the enantiomer of a molecule: Switch **ALL** chiral centers (from R to S) (or S to R)

Easiest way to do this? Switch **two groups** on each center.

(NOTE: Switching **two** *pairs* of groups on a chiral center
turns it back into its original orientation. Prove this to yourself
with your model kit in your spare time.)

138

Practice (R, S)

Draw the two enantiomers of 2-bromopentane

Practice (R, S)

Draw the two enantiomers of **1-bromo-2-methylbutane**

Laura Lanni

Which are enantiomer pairs?

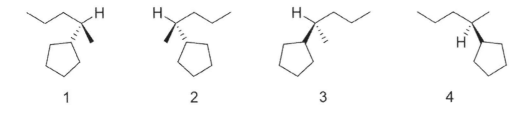

1   2   3   4

141

MESO compound (a subset of achiral molecules)

An achiral molecule with **>1** stereogenic centers = meso compound

The mirror image of a meso compound is not its stereoisomer; it is the SAME molecule.

(Recall: achiral compound has an internal mirror plane)

Example: 2R,3S-butanediol can be described as achiral and meso.

Build it, rotate along C2-C3 bond, (label R,S). Perhaps a Newman projection can help you see the internal mirror plane.

OH

OH

142

MESO, example continued: 2R,3S-butanediol

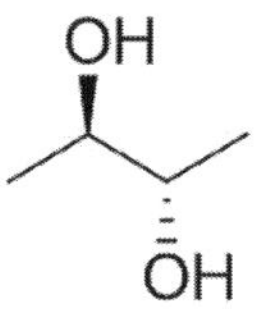

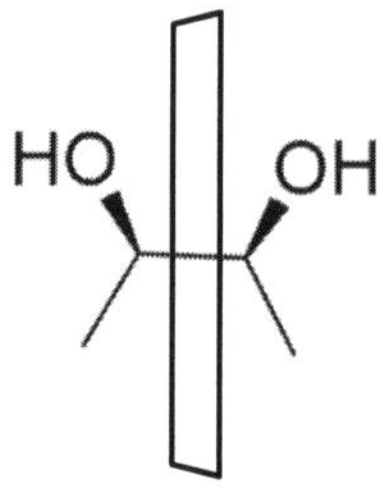

same molecule rotated to
show symmetry
molecule is achiral
molecule is meso

143

R,R and S,S forms of 2,3-butanediol

are NOT achiral because they have no plane of symmetry
("not achiral" is a double negative that means chiral)
Draw the R,R and the S,S form of 2,3-butanediol.

They are enantiometers of each other and they are diastereomers of the meso R,S form from previous example.

144

Stereoisomer pairings

Enantiomers:

Nonsuperimposable mirror images

change ALL chiral centers

Diastereomers:

Nonsuperimposable non-mirror images

change SOME (but not all) chiral centers

MORE examples and details of molecules with multiple chiral centers

How many stereoisomers are possible? Maximum 2^n where n = number of chiral centers

Example: Draw all stereoisomers of 2-bromo-4-chlorohexane

(label R,S. Indicate enantiomer pairs and diastereomer pairs.)

Molecules with multiple chiral centers

Another example: Draw, label absolute configuration, indicate enantiomer and diastereomer pairs of **1-chloro-3-methylcyclohexane**

Fischer projections

Like Newman Projections, Fischer projections are standardized depictions of molecules that are useful for visualizing stereoisomers, especially those with multiple chiral centers.

Example: Build this with your model kit
and label all stereocenters R or S.

Draw as a Fischer projection,
then draw the Fischer projection of the enantiomer.

Fischer projections of tartaric acid HOOCCHOHCHOHCOOH

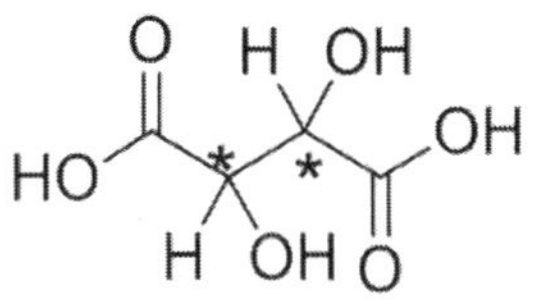

Draw RR, SS, RS, SR tartaric acid.

Label absolute configurations and indicate enantiomeric and diastereomeric pairs.
Consider this: are there really 4 different stereoisomers?

149

Fischer projections of tartaric acid HOOCCHOHCHOHCOOH

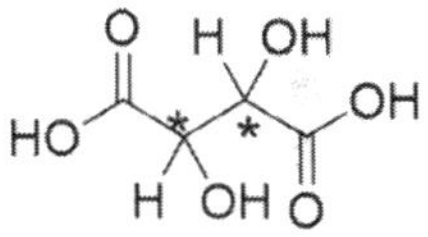

draw RR, SS, RS, SR tartaric acid

There are actually only THREE stereoisomers of tartaric acid, because ___ and ___ are identical to each other (meso).

150

Fischer projections of tartaric acid HOOCCHOHCHOHCOOH

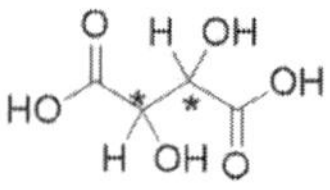

draw Fischer projections of RR, SS, RS, SR tartaric acid

Enantiomer pairs

Diastereomer pairs

__ = __. Identical (because meso, have internal mirror plane, are achiral), same molecule

151

Racemic mix

50:50 mix of a pair of enantiomers

The pair of enantiomers in equal concentrations are called "racemates," and are called a "racemic mix."

152

Physical properties of enantiomers and diastereomers

Enantiomers have the same physical properties (boiling point, melting point, solubilities), but they do not interact with plane-polarized light the same way.

Diastereomers have different physical properties.

153

Rotation of plane polarized light (PPL) in a polarimeter

Achiral molecules and racemic mixes do not rotate plane polarized light. They are not optically active.

Solutions of pure chiral molecules *do* rotate plane polarized light. They are *OPTICALLY ACTIVE*.

If one enantiomer rotates PPL one way, its enantiomer will rotate the PPL the same number of degrees in the opposite way, giving a net rotation of 0 degrees.

154

Enantiomeric excess

Enantiomeric excess, also known as *optical purity*

Calculation of enantiomeric excess "ee"

ee = $\dfrac{\text{observed specific rotation (of light passed through solution in a polarimeter)}}{\text{specific rotation of the single pure enantiomer}}$ x 100

Ex: Racemic mix: 50:50 mix of two enantiomers,
    will have no net rotation of PPL,
    so numerator = 0,
    so ee = 0
meaning no excess of one enantiomer over the other;
both enantiomers are in equal concentration.

155

example

A mixture of two enantiomers is 25% R and 75% S. What is the enantiomeric excess (ee)?

156

Another enantiomeric excess example

If observed specific rotation for a solution is +9.2°, and the pure S stereoisomer's rotation is +23.1°, calculate the enantiomeric excess of the S stereoisomer in the solution.

$$ee = (+9.2°/+23.1°) \times 100$$
$$= 40\% \text{ S excess}$$

Does that mean the mixture contains 40% S and 60% R?

That makes no senses if S is IN EXCESS.

Think think think... There is 70% S and 30% R (math). 40% more S than R.

157

Recognize special chiral molecules without standard sp³ chiral centers

The presence of a chiral center is not necessary for a compound to be chiral.
Examples:

Atropisomers

Allenes

enantiomers

Spirocenters

enantiomers

158

Medicines/drugs with chiral centers

159

acetaminophen

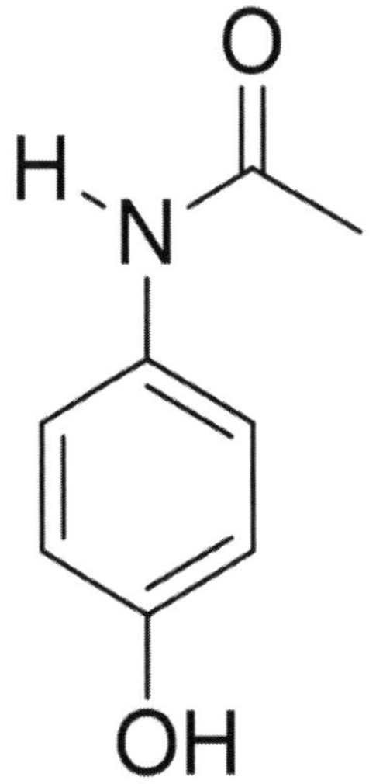

160

S-Naproxen

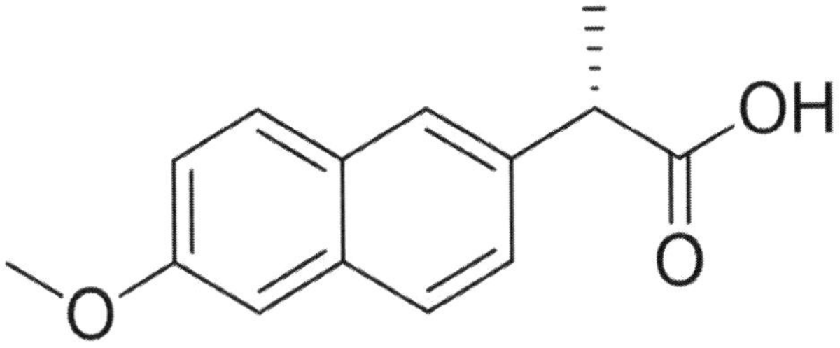

161

Ibuprofen

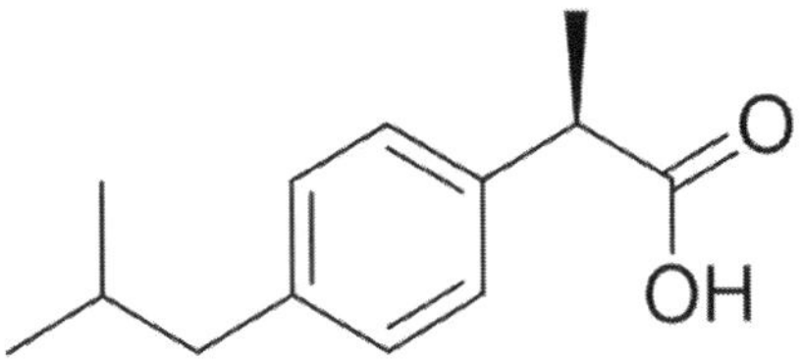

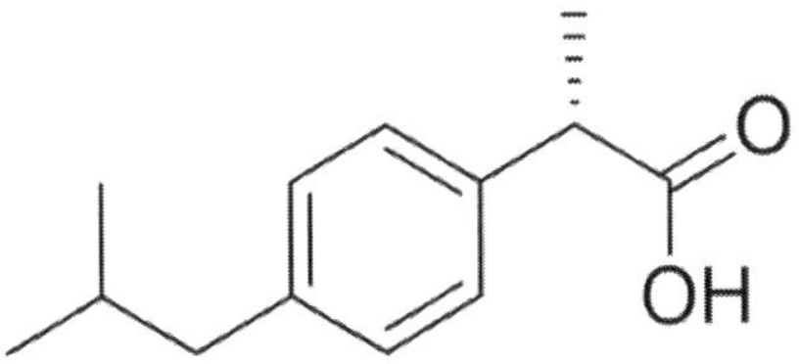

162

methamphetamine

One stereoisomer is the neurotoxin/psychostimulant and the other is not.

163

thalidomide

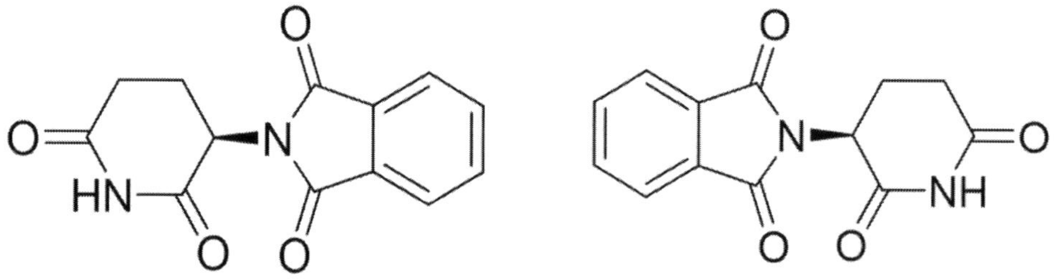

164

Amoxicillin

clarithromycin

Lipitor

cholesterol

Calculate the maximum number of possible stereoisomers of cholesterol...

The Study of Chemical Reactions

connections between general and organic chemistry

Review from general chemistry as needed by reading text chapter__:

Endothermic and exothermic reactions

Enthalpy and entropy and Gibb's Free Energy

Bond dissociation energy

Equilibrium

Kinetics, order, activation energy

As noted in the course syllabus: After stereochemistry, the rest of the course is about organic chemical reactions, their intermediates, transition states, reaction coordinate diagrams, rate laws, stereoselectivity, regioselectivity, and mechanisms. The topics in Chapter __ will be discussed as needed during the subsequent chapters but is included here as a resource and reference for you during your study. Basic mechanisms may be discussed during lecture.

169

General chemistry review: Enthalpy (ΔH)

Energy diagrams for **exothermic** vs. **endothermic** reactions

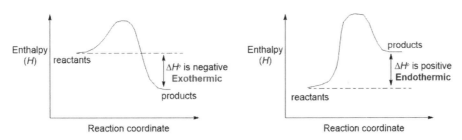

Products lower in energy than reactants
Energy is released as heat
   (PE converted to KE)
$\Delta H°$ is negative
Temperature of surroundings increases

Products higher in energy than reactants
Energy is consumed
   (KE converted to PE)
$\Delta H°$ is positive
Temperature of surroundings decreases

6-170

general chemistry Review: Kinetics

Recall that a (−) sign for ΔG tells us a process is product favored. (It is spontaneous in the indicated direction.)

That does NOT tell us anything about the RATE or **kinetics** for the process.
   ΔG does not indicate how fast a reaction will occur.

Some spontaneous processes are fast, such as explosions.

Some spontaneous processes are slow such as C (diamond) → C (graphite)... this takes millions of years, even though a spontaneous reaction.

general chemistry Review: Kinetics

The **order** of a reaction is represented by exponents x and y
$$Rate = k \, [A]^x[B]^y$$

Rate = k [A] First order If [A] is doubled rate is doubled	Rate = k [A][B] second order overall first order for A, first order for B If [A] is doubled rate is doubled	Rate = k [A]^2[B] third order overall second order for A, first order for B If [A] is doubled rate is quadrupled

general chemistry Review: Reading Energy Diagrams

Kinetics (reaction rate) depend on size of energy barrier called activation energy, E_a
Thermodynamics (spontaneity/equilibrium) depends on sign of Gibbs Free energy change, ΔG

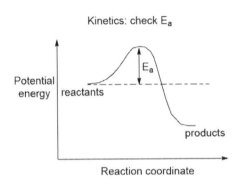

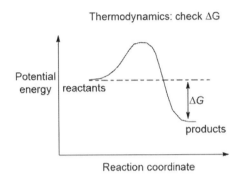

6-173

General chemistry Review: another example

Consider two reaction pathways for A + B:

A+B → C + D   or   A + B → E + F

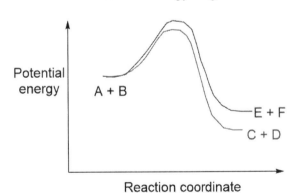

What does energy diagram tell us?

Which pathway occurs faster? (and how can you tell?)

Which products are more stable? (and how can you tell?)

6-174

General chemistry Review: Kinetics vs. Thermodynamics

Consider two reaction pathways for A + B:

A+B → C + D   or   A + B → E + F

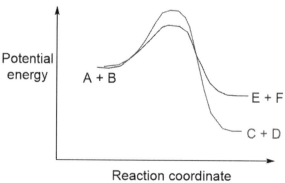

What does energy diagram tell us?

Which pathway occurs faster? (and how can you tell?)

Which products are more stable? (and how can you tell?)

General chemistry Review: Transition States vs. Intermediates

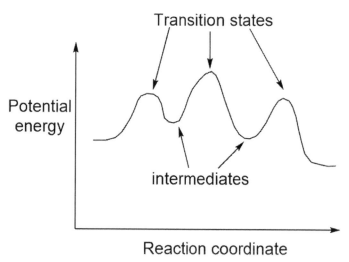

A **transition state** is the high energy state a reaction passes through during an elementary step. Transition states are fleeting; they <u>cannot</u> be observed but we can draw them by representing the transition as bonds are broken and formed during an elementary step. On an energy diagram, transition states are indicated by an energy maxima.

An **intermediate** is a species formed during an elementary step in a reaction mechanism. They are indicated energy minima on the diagram. Intermediates are observable. They are actual chemical species that are formed in one elementary step and consumed in a subsequent step.

Reaction Mechanisms

Organic chemists study HOW reactions occur as a part of understanding kinetics of a reaction.

A **reaction mechanism** is a series of elementary steps that shows how a reaction occurs by using curved arrows to indicate "electron flow" for *breaking and making bonds*.

177

Reaction Mechanism details

Each step in the mechanism is an **elementary step**—it involves only one transition state.

An **intermediate** is formed from one elementary step and is consumed in a subsequent step.

A **transition state** exists at the point of maximum potential energy during an elementary step.

The **molecularity** of an elementary step is the number of particles which react.

The **RATE** of a reaction is determined by its slowest step. (the one with largest activation energy, Kinetics, General chemistry)

A **1st order** reaction is unimolecular.

A **2nd order** reaction is bimolecular.

178

Reaction Mechanism MORE details

Electrophiles are electron poor and electron loving.
Mechanism curved arrows END at the electrophile.

Nucleophiles are electron rich and nucleus loving.
Mechanism curved arrows BEGIN at the nucleophile.

The arrows always begi**N** at the **Nucleophile**
and **E**nd at the **Electrophile**.

Nucleophiles

electron rich species
can **donate a pair of electrons** to form a bond
Lewis bases

Examples of nucleophiles

Electrophiles

electron deficient species,
can **accept a pair of electrons** to form a bond
Lewis acids

Examples
   Carbocations

partially-positive atoms like carbons bonded to halogens in alkyl halides

carbons bonded to oxygen in ketones, aldehydes, and other carbonyl-containing functional groups

181

Mechanism/Elementary Step Examples

In a reaction mechanism, curved arrows are used to show how electrons move as bonds are broken and formed.

$$B: \quad + \quad H-A \quad \rightleftharpoons \quad B-H \quad + \quad A:$$

B⁻ is nucleophile; H$^{\delta+}$ is electrophile   B-H bond formed; A kept a pair of electrons

Examples of elementary steps:
   Nucleophilic attack
   Loss of a leaving group
   Proton transfers
   Rearrangements

182

Laura Lanni   91

Mechanism/Elementary Step Examples: Nucleophilic attack

Examples

- nucleophile attacks electrophile, both have full charges

The tail of the arrow starts on the electrons on the nucleophile.
The head of the arrow ends on a nucleus of an electrophile.
The electrons end up being shared rather than transferred and a new bond is formed.

- nucleophile attacks electrophile, both have partial charges due to polar bonds

To make a new sigma bond, the electrophilic carbon of the acid chloride
  must break its π bond so it does not exceed an octet.
Note the two formal charges on the product of this elementary step.

nucleophilic oxygen
electron rich

electrophilic carbon
electron poor (deficient)

- Electron rich π bond as nucleophile

A pair of electrons in a π bond can act as nucleophile
The σ bond remained intact.

183

Mechanism/Elementary Step Examples: loss of leaving group

Carbon halogen bond breaks; the bromide is the leaving group and it takes the electron pair when it leaves.

Carbon-halogen bond breaks as carbon-oxygen double bond forms; the chloride is the leaving group and it take the electron pair when it leaves.

184

Mechanism/Elementary Step Examples: Proton transfers

REVIEW! We have already seen these in acid base reactions.

Note the common theme...electron flow from rich (-) to poor (+), relieving charges, forming charges...formal charge calculations should become automatic.

Mechanism/Elementary Step Examples: carbocation rearrangement

Rearrangements of carbocations less substituted to more substituted.
Shifts can only occur from adjacent carbons.
Shifts occur only to produce a more stable (more substituted) carbocation.

1,2-hydride shift
Notice the hydride (H:⁻) moves *with* the sigma bond electrons.
This example changes a secondary carbocation to a more stable tertiary carbocation

1,2-alkyl shift
Notice the methyl (H₃C:⁻)) moves *with* the sigma bond electrons.
This example also changes a secondary carbocation to a more stable tertiary carbocation

Mechanism/Elementary Step Examples:
a complete mechanism example

A complete mechanism shows the electron flow (arrow pushing) of a sequence of elementary steps. All *formal charges are included.*

leaving group leaves   carbocation rearrangement   nucleophilic attack   proton transfer

Beginner's practice mechanism: be able to start with a series of steps like this and add appropriate arrows and label elementary steps.

187

Notes about drawing curved arrows in mechanisms: common student errors while learning mechanisms

- Curved arrow must start on a pair of electrons (a lone pair, or a shared pair).

- The head of a curved arrow shows either the formation of a bond, or formation of a lone pair.

- The head of a curved arrow can never show carbon (or other Period 2 element) forming more than four bonds. (Carbon cannot exceed the octet.)

188

substitution and elimination reactions

Preview of 1st and 2nd order substitution and elimination

S_N1	E1	vs	E2	S_N2

S_N1	E1	E2	S_N2
1st order	1st order	2nd order	2nd order
2 steps	2 steps	1 step (concerted)	1 step (concerted)
Unimolecular slow step	**Unimolecular** slow step	**Bimolecular** slow step	**Bimolecular** slow step
Rate = k[R-LG]	Rate = k[R-LG]	Rate = k[R-LG][**BASE**]	Rate = k[R-LG][**nuc**]
(independent of [**nuc**])	(independent of [**BASE**])		
RXN coord diagram: 2 humps	RXN coord diagram: 2 humps	RXN coord diagram: 1 hump (concerted reaction)	RXN coord diagram: 1 hump (concerted reaction)
3° (and 2°) substrates	3° substrates	1° or 2° or 3° substrates	Methyl, 1° or 2° substrates
Forms carbocation intermediate	Forms carbocation intermediate	NO carbocation formed	NO carbocation intermediate
C+ rearrangement possible	C+ rearrangement possible		

S_N1	E1	E2	S_N2
Stereochemical outcome: ~50:50 mix (**racemic**)	Stereochemical outcome: E over Z	Stereochemical outcome: Dependent on **antiperiplanar** orientation of H and LG	Stereochemical outcome: **inversion** at electrophilic carbon
Polar protic solvents like water, MeOH, etc.	Regiochemical outcomes: Zaitsev or Hofmann	Regiochemical outcomes: Zaitsev or Hofmann	**Polar aprotic** solvents like DMF, DMSO, CH$_3$CN, acetone, etc.

Product of E1 and E2 eliminations: **alkene**

189

190

Leaving Groups

Good leaving groups are
- conjugate bases of strong acids
- weak bases
- stable

	Acid	pK_a		Conjugate base	as leaving group?
strongest acid	H—I	-11	most stable base	I$^\ominus$	BEST!
	H—Br	-9		Br$^\ominus$	
	H—Cl	-7		Cl$^\ominus$	
	(tosyl) S—OH	-3		(tosyl) S—O$^\ominus$	good leaving groups
	H$_3$O$^\oplus$	-2		H$_2$O	
	H—F	3		F$^\ominus$	
	H$_2$O...H	15.7		O...H$^\ominus$	
	...O—H	16		...O$^\ominus$	poor leaving groups
	...O—H	18		...O$^\ominus$	
weakest acid	H$_2$N—H$_2$	38	least stable base	H$_2$N$^\ominus$	WORST!

191

Alkyl halide (RX) as reactant (substrate) focus on trend of halogen (X) leaving groups

$$F^- \ll Cl^- < Br^- < I^-$$

Least reactive RX-------------------→most reactive RX

Slowest--------------------------------------→ fastest rate

Poorest LG--------------------------------------→ best LG

192

REVIEW Primary (1°), secondary (2°) and tertiary (3°) compounds (RX and ROH)

Pattern

On carbon where OH or X is bonded, there are

#H	designation	(#R groups)
2	1° (primary)	(1)
1	2° (secondary)	(2)
0	3° (tertiary)	(3)

(R = alkyl group)

193

Primary (1°), secondary (2°) and tertiary (3°) compounds (RX and ROH)

Primary alcohol

Primary alkyl halide

Secondary alcohol

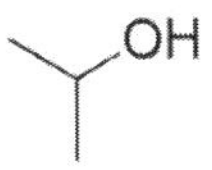

Secondary alkyl halide

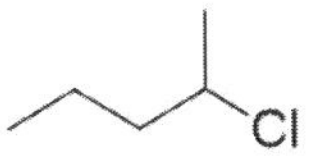

Tertiary alcohol

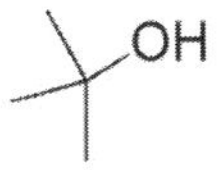

Tertiary alkyl halide

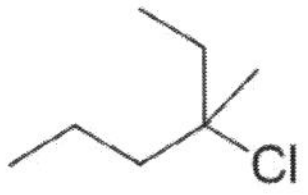

194

REVIEW Alkyl halides (R-X)

"Functional" group, nomenclature

Practice

Name these alkyl halides.

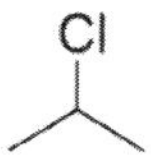

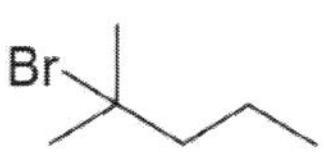

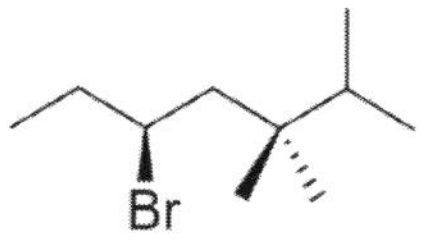

Are these names correct?

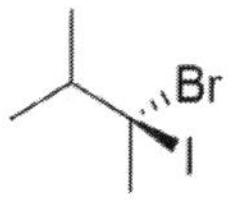

(S)-2-bromo-2-iodo-3-methylbutane

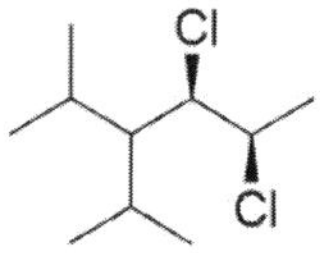

(2R,3R)-2,3-dichloro-4-isopropyl-5-methylhexane

Laura Lanni

98

Enough review
BEGIN REACTIONS ON ALKYL HALIDES

197

Substitution
a nucleophile takes the place of a leaving group
A new functional group is formed.

$$R\text{-}LG + nuc^- \rightarrow R\text{-}nuc \ (+ \ LG^-)$$

Elimination
a base takes a proton from a carbon adjacent to one that loses a leaving group.
An alkene is formed.

$$R\text{-}LG + base \rightarrow alkene \ (+ \ H\text{-}base + LG^-)$$

198

Substitution and Elimination reactions can both take place *via* 1st- or 2nd-order kinetics

Two substitution reaction types: S_N1 and S_N2

S_N means nucleophilic substitution

1 or 2 indicates 1st or 2nd order kinetics

Two elimination reaction types: E1 and E2

E stands for elimination

1 or 2 indicates 1st or 2nd order kinetics

199

Substitution reaction introductory examples

Preview some examples: Draw the product when methyl bromide reacts with each *via* a substitution reaction.

a. Sodium hydroxide

b. Potassium ethoxide

c. Sodium benzoate

d. Potassium cyanide

e. Sodium iodide

200

S$_N$2 MECHANISM and example

201

S$_N$2

nucleophilic bimolecular substitution

Mechanism is ONE concerted elementary step: nucleophile attacks AT THE SAME TIME the leaving group leaves.

The reaction coordinate diagram has only one hump.

Draw the transition state.

202

S$_N$2

Reaction rate is dependent on BOTH the concentrations of the [alkyl halide (RX) (electrophilic substrate)] **and** the [nucleophile]

$$\text{Rate} = k[RX][\text{nuc}^-]$$

1st order for *substrate* (alkyl halide) and 1st order for *nucleophile*, so overall 1+1 = **2nd order**

(example with mechanism)

203

S$_N$2 stereochemistry

inversion at electrophilic (possibly stereogenic/chiral) carbon due to backside attack by nucleophile.

nucleophile ———→ —leaving group
backside attack

Example: Hydroxide reacts with 2*R*-bromoheptane

204

S$_N$2 steric effects (crowding)

Fastest second order nucleophilic substitutions occur with less crowding (less sterics) on the **alkyl halide** (because the nucleophile needs room to attack the electrophilic carbon)

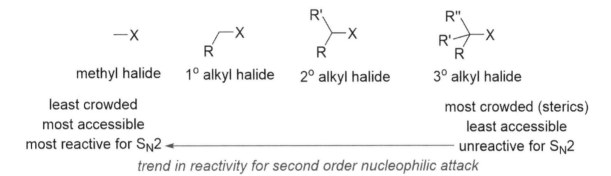

methyl halide   1° alkyl halide   2° alkyl halide   3° alkyl halide

least crowded
most accessible
most reactive for S$_N$2 ←   most crowded (sterics)
least accessible
→ unreactive for S$_N$2

trend in reactivity for second order nucleophilic attack

205

S$_N$2 steric effects (crowding)

Fastest second order nucleophilic substitutions occur with less crowding (less sterics) on the **alkyl halide** (because the nucleophile needs room to attack the electrophilic carbon)

Show me data to back this up...

$$R-Br \xrightarrow{\text{I}^-, \text{ in acetone at room temperature}} R-I \ + \ Br^-$$

R	substrate structure	relative rate
CH$_3$	—Br	145
CH$_3$CH$_2$	/—Br	1
isopropyl	>—Br	0.008
t-butyl	>—Br	negligible

206

Review kinetics for S$_N$2

Faster reactions have lower activation energy on slow elementary step.

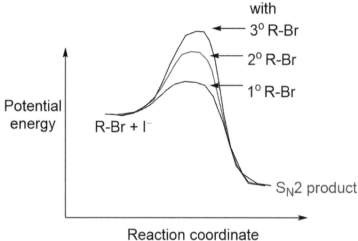

Nucleophiles for S$_N$2

better nucleophiles

⟵

I⁻   Br⁻   Cl⁻   HS⁻   HO⁻   ⁻CN   H₂O   ROH

full negative charge   partial negative charge

Nucleophiles are often anions but can be neutral like water, dimethylsulfide, alcohol

Nucleophilicity—how good is the nucleophile?

How quickly will it donate its electron pair? kinetic consideration

1. Comparison by charge: anions better than neutral (when nucleophilic atom is same)

   Examples, comparisons: hydroxide vs water; ethoxide vs ethanol

2. Stronger base = more nucleophilic, less stable base (when the attacking atoms are the same size)

   Examples, comparisons using pK_a: ethoxide vs acetate

Solvents for 2nd order substitutions

Polar aprotic solvents are best for S_N2 reactions

(Polar PROTIC solvents are poor for S_N2: they "cage" the nucleophile, stabilize it, and inhibit it from nucleophilic attack—thus slowing the second order substitution reaction.)

Aprotic solvent can stabilize both cations and anions.

Polar protic solvents	Polar aprotic solvents (better for S_N2)
water	acetone
Methanol and ethanol and other alcohols	dimethylformamide
ammonia	dimethylsulfoxide
Acetic acid	acetonitrile

209

Solvents for 2nd order substitutions

In aprotic solvents, nucleophiles are less stable, more reactive.

Activation energy will be *lower*.

Substitution reaction will be *faster*.

Aprotic solvents are best for S_N2 reactions.

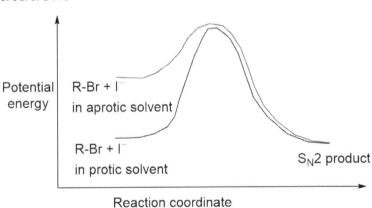

210

Recap S_N2

Concerted (1-step) reaction: nucleophile attacks as the leaving group leaves

Depends on nucleophile's ability to attack *and* leaving group's ability to leave.

Better nucleophiles have negative (−) charge, are generally stronger bases

Sterics (alkyl crowding) on substrate slows the S_N2 reaction

   Best RX substrates: Methyl > 1° > 2°

Protic solvents cage nucleophile and slow the reaction (so aprotic solvents are better)

Inversion at chiral α electrophilic carbon on substrate (must consider stereochemistry)

211

Practice

1. Write the S_N2 mechanism for the reaction of hydroxide with 2S-iodopentane.

2. Name the product.

212

practice

1. Which is a better nucleophile?

        HO- or HS-

A. HO-
B. HS-
C. no difference

2. Which is a stronger base?

        HO- or HS-

A. HO-
B. HS-
C. no difference

3. Which is the major organic product of this SN2 reaction?

NaCN in DMSO

A.   B.   C.

More PRACTICE: Stereochemistry review (don't forget what you used to know)

Which are pairs of enantiomers
Which are pairs of diastereomers?
Are any identical?

1.   2.   3.   4.

What is the relationship between these Fischer projections?

Unimolecular Nucleophilic Substitution: S_N1

The rate determining (slow) elementary step is **unimolecular** (that's where the 1 comes from)

Formation of the carbocation is the **rate determining step** (SLOW step)

The carbocation is an **intermediate**.

The mechanism is **two steps** so the reaction coordinate diagram has two peaks.

Be able to draw both **transition states**.

215

S_N1 MECHANISM and example

216

S$_N$1 reaction coordinate diagram, rate law

The rate law for any elementary step can be written from its molecularity. (from general chemistry)

For the previous carbocation formation step, the rate law can be written:
Rate = k [RX]
order = 1
k = rate constant

S$_N$1 is a first order reaction—rate is dependent **only** on concentration of the substrate (alkyl halide RX in this case)

The mechanism shows two steps: leaving group leaves (slowly) folloed by nucleophilic attack (fast). Reaction coordinate diagram:

217

S$_N$1 carbocation intermediate

A reaction may only proceed as fast as its slowest elementary step
For S$_N$1, the slow step is formation of the carbocation

alkyl chloride substrate   carbocation intermediate

218

Carbocations

All carbocations (C^+) are trigonal planar, sp^2 hybridized with one empty unhybridized p orbital

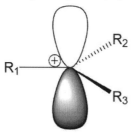

Carbocations are reactive intermediates in the S_N1 (and E1) mechanisms—they are formed (slowly) in the first step and consumed (rapidly) in a subsequent step.

219

Carbocation (C^+) stability

More alkyl groups on a carbocation make it more stable

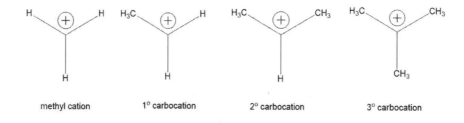

least stable_____most stable

Reason for stability trend? *dispersal of + charge on central C (delocalization) due to* **induction** and **hyperconjugation**

220

Induction

Alkyl groups on the central C⁺ help delocalize the charge by induction and hyperconjugation

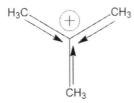

each methyl is an electron donating group, and donates
electrons through induction (through σ bond) which helps
stabilize the + charge.

Hyperconjugation

Alkyl groups on the central C⁺ help delocalize the charge by induction and hyperconjugation

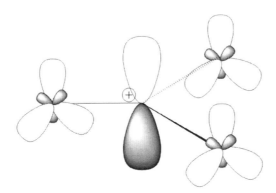

Look at carbocation stability trend again

 # σ bonds that can hyperconjugate and stabilize the C⁺ charge

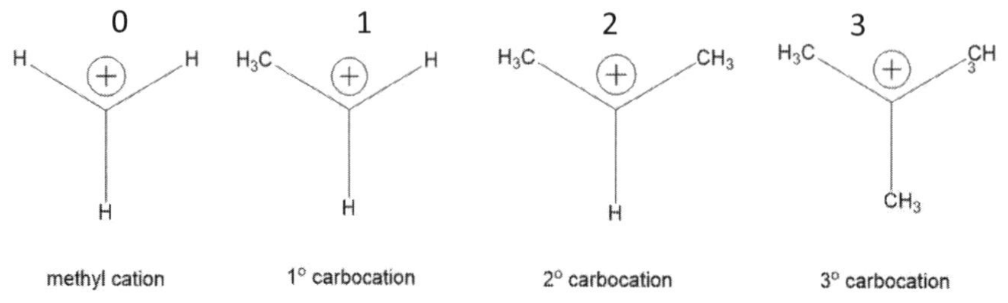

| 0 | 1 | 2 | 3 |
| methyl cation | 1° carbocation | 2° carbocation | 3° carbocation |

least stable_____most stable

More σ bonds from carbocation center to alkyl groups (NOT H) = more stable carbocation.

223

practice carbocation rearrangements—what happened?

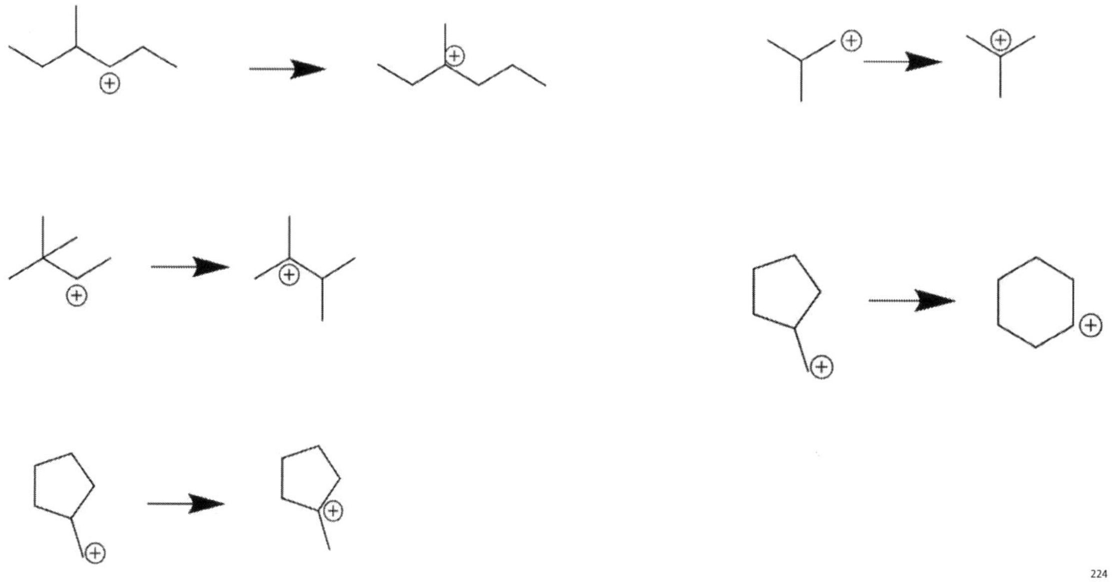

224

S_N1: beware C+ rearrangement

Example

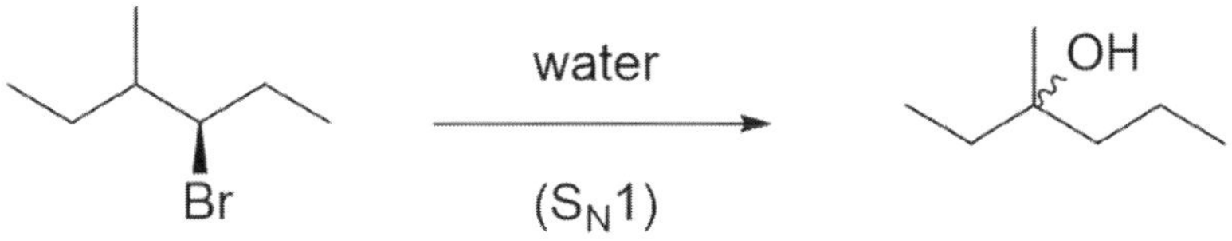

water

(S$_N$1)

225

solvolysis

Reaction where solvent acts as a reagent (reactant) [See previous reaction where water was the nucleophile and solvent]

Examples:

Water acting as both the solvent and the nucleophile for a substitution reaction (aka *hydrolysis*)

alcohol acting as both the solvent and the base for elimination reactions (aka *alcoholysis*) (later)

226

carbocation intermediate, stereochemical outcome
S_N1: STEREOselectivity

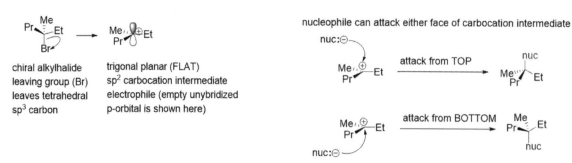

chiral alkylhalide
leaving group (Br)
leaves tetrahedral
sp³ carbon

trigonal planar (FLAT)
sp² carbocation intermediate
electrophile (empty unybridized
p-orbital is shown here)

nucleophile can attack either face of carbocation intermediate

227

Solvent effects on first-order substitutions (S_N1)

RECALL: S_N2 reactions are faster in **polar aprotic** solvents.

NEW: S_N1 reactions can be sped up in polar protic solvents like water, alcohols, ammonia, or acetic acid

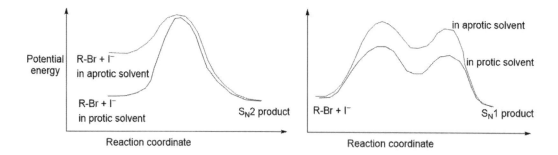

228

RECAP of 1ˢᵗ and 2ⁿᵈ order substitution reactions

S_N1 E1   vs   E2 S_N2

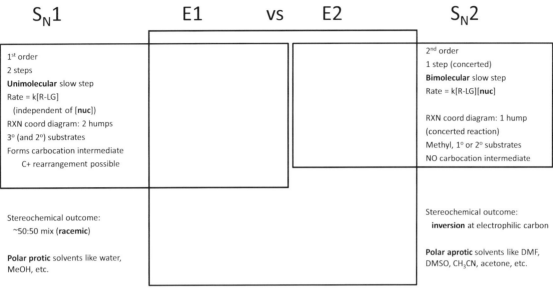

1ˢᵗ order
2 steps
Unimolecular slow step
Rate = k[R-LG]
  (independent of [**nuc**])
RXN coord diagram: 2 humps
3° (and 2°) substrates
Forms carbocation intermediate
    C+ rearrangement possible

Stereochemical outcome:
  ~50:50 mix (**racemic**)

Polar protic solvents like water,
MeOH, etc.

2ⁿᵈ order
1 step (concerted)
Bimolecular slow step
Rate = k[R-LG][**nuc**]

RXN coord diagram: 1 hump
(concerted reaction)
Methyl, 1° or 2° substrates
NO carbocation intermediate

Stereochemical outcome:
  inversion at electrophilic carbon

Polar aprotic solvents like DMF,
DMSO, CH₃CN, acetone, etc.

229

Elimination reactions

230

Elimination reactions: dehydrohalogenation of RX (alkyl halide) to make alkene

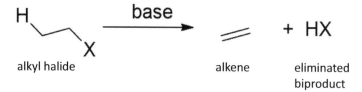

Requires alkoxide base like NaOMe in MeOH, or potassium t-butoxide (K O-t-Bu) in DMSO, and in some reactions KOH in EtOH is strong enough.

Regioselective and Stereoselective considerations

Can be 1st or 2nd order (E1 or E2)

Rate laws, transition states

Reaction coordinate diagrams parallel substitution reactions

231

E2 MECHANISM and example

232

Alkenes

Recall alkenes have a carbon-carbon double bond

(1 σ and 1 π bond)

The carbons in the double bond are sp^2 hybridized

Alkene general formula C_nH_{2n}

Name: start with # to indicate where double bond starts, and end with –ene suffix

233

Alkene nomenclature

#-prefix-ene

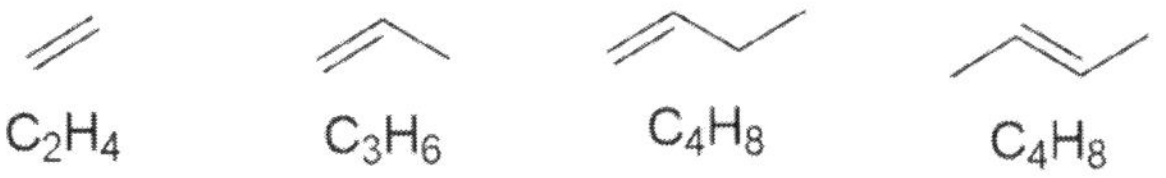

C_2H_4 C_3H_6 C_4H_8 C_4H_8

234

Alkene nomenclature

Branched alkenes: give the double bond priority over branches in numbering

Alkene nomenclature

If alkene AND alcohol, OH takes precedence in numbering.

Alkene nomenclature

For cycloalkene, it is *understood* that the double bond connects C1 and C2

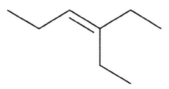

Practice/review

1. What is the molecular formula?

2. What is the IUPAC name?

3. How many sp² hybridized carbons?

4. How many sp³ hybridized carbons?

5. How many σ bonds between sp² and sp³ orbitals?

6. How many Csp²-Hs are there?

E and Z Isomerism in alkenes

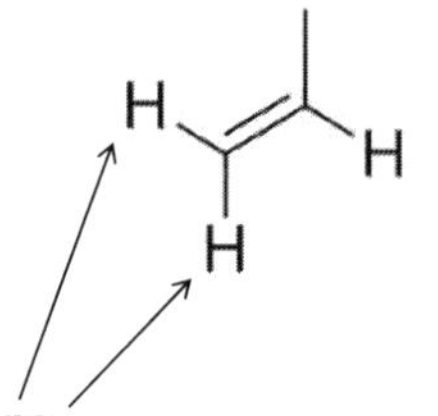

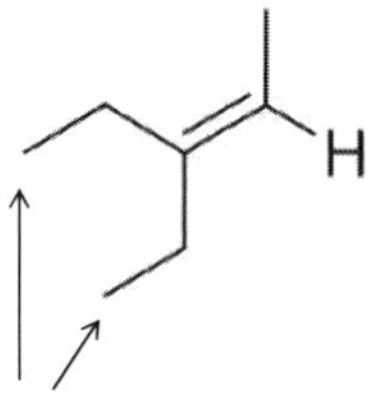

2 hydrogens   2 ethyls

so each of these alkenes has only 1 possible structure and *no E or Z designation*

E an Z isomerism occurs when *neither carbon in double bond has 2 of the same groups.*

Example

239

E/Z Isomerism in alkenes

More examples

240

Use Cahn-Ingold-Prelog Priority Rules (same as for R and S determination)

On each carbon in the double bond, rank the 2 substituents based on atomic number until ties are broken.

Look at positions of the two higher ranking groups and assign

        E (across the double bond)

     or Z (zame side of double bond).

Example: E-2-pentene

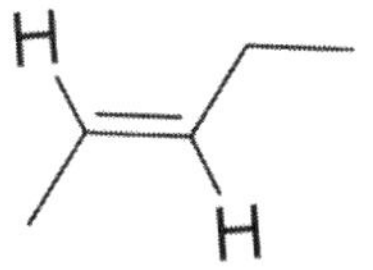

E/Z examples

E or Z?

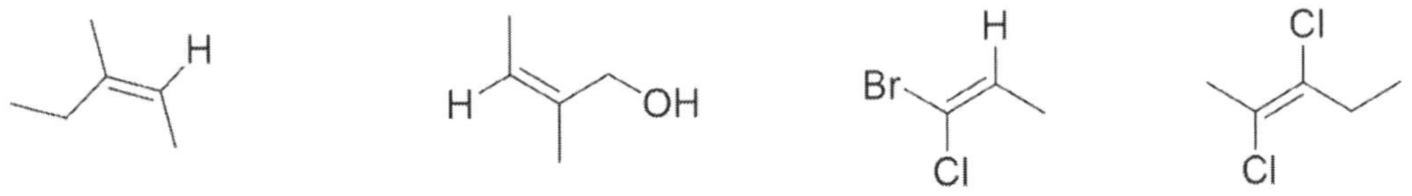

Backwards: Draw alkene structure from name

Draw the structure of (E)-1-bromopropene

Relative stabilities of alkenes

Alkene sp^2 carbons with **more ALKYL GROUPS** make alkene **more stable**

unsubstituted		least stable
mono-substituted		
di-substituted		
tri-substituted		
tetra-substituted		most stable

Laura Lanni

Relative stabilities of alkenes

Alkenes with more highly substituted double bonds are more stable—WHY?

Hint: Think about electronics and sterics.

Example: Compare *trans*-2-butene to *cis*-2-butene

245

Practice (before next lecture or recitation, whichever comes first)

Draw and name as many **alkene isomers** of C_6H_{12} as possible. (More than 10)

246

Back to E2

Mechanism is 1 step, **concerted**, no carbocation formed, bimolecular

Rate = k[alkyl halide][base]   (second order overall, so rate of reaction depends on concentrations of both substrate and base)

Be able to draw reaction coordinate diagram and transition state.

Regioselective: More stable alkene will be major product: more substituted double bond, E isomer (can control with base choice.)

Stereoselective: Leaving group (X) MUST BE ANTIPERIPLANAR to H. (NEWMAN projection can help.)

Regioselectivity of E2 reactions

A substrate (alkyl halide) with more than one adjacent carbon that can be deprotonated by a strong base may result in more than one alkene product.

When constitutional isomers are formed as the products of a reaction, with one of them as the major product, the reaction is **regioselective**.

Example: dehydrohalogenation of 2-bromo-2-methylbutane with sodium ethoxide

71%	29%
major product	minor product
more stable, more substituted alkene	less stable, less substituted alkene
Zaitsev product	Hofmann product

How can we change the reaction to make the Hofmann product the major product?

Practice for you: Review mechanism, transition states, rate law as needed to get to each product.

Laura Lanni

Practice: Dehydrohalogenation E2 examples

2-bromo-2,3-dimethylbutane $\xrightarrow[\text{MeOH}]{\text{NaOMe}}$

1-bromo-3-methylbutane $\xrightarrow[\text{DMSO}]{K^+ \ ^\ominus O\text{-}C(CH_3)_3}$

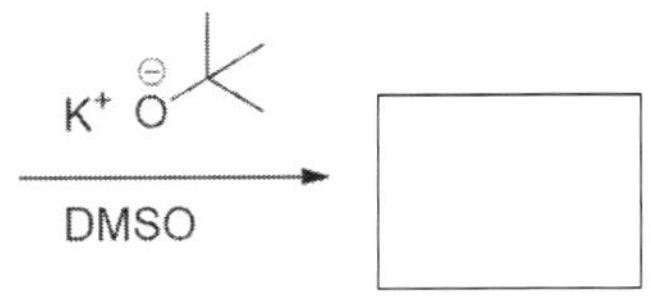

Practice E2

For each E2 reaction, draw the likely mixture of products but clearly indicate the major product.

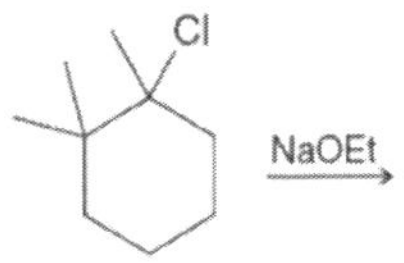

$\xrightarrow{\text{NaOEt}}$

$\xrightarrow{\text{NaOH}}$

Laura Lanni

125

More Stereoselectivity for E2: E (*trans*) vs Z (*cis*) alkene products

Dehydrohalogenation of 3-bromopropane makes two possible products:

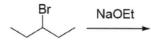

Trans product is more stable.

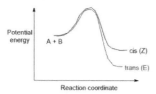

E2 Stereospecificity: halogen and adjacent hydrogen must be *antiperiplanar* for concerted reaction to occur (Use Newman projections)

Examples

Laura Lanni

E2 Stereospecificity: halogen and adjacent hydrogen must be *antiperiplanar* for concerted reaction to occur (Use Newman projections)

Examples

More examples/discussion of E2 anti requirement

Alkyl halides will rotate around σ bonds to MAKE H and LG anti to each other.

E2 mechanism is not always possible in cyclo alkyl halides in which anti position (halogen and β-hydrogen) must be 1,2 diaxial

base → No reaction. No alkene produced.

Draw chair and/or build model to see why.

More examples/discussion of E2 anti requirement: consider the cyclohexane chair

Dehydrohalogenation of Bromocyclohexane with base:

Due to antiperiplanar requirement, E2 can only happen when the leaving group (Br) and adjacent H are 1,2-diaxial.

practice

1. Consider the following S$_N$2 reaction:

   What is the configuration of the chiral center on the product?

   NaCN
   DMF

   A. R
   B. S
   C. Not chiral

2. Which Newman projection viewed along the C2-C3 bond shows the antiperiplanar ("anti") conformation for this molecule required for E2 dehydrohalogenation?

   A)   B)

   C)   D)

3. Which is the correct structure of the product for this E2 dehydrohalogenation?

   base →

   A)   C)

   B)   D)

Laura Lanni   128

Practice: More consideration of E2 antiperiplanar requirement

Which of the two molecules below will NOT be able to undergo E2 elimination with strong base? Why not?
(Perhaps redraw in chair configuration and/or build with a model kit. Consider antiperiplanar means Cl and adjacent H must be 1,2-diaxial on the ring.)

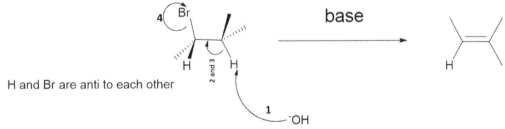

257

RECAP/ E2 concerted mechanism--dehydrohalogenation showing anti-elimination

Dehydrohalogenation of 2S-bromo-3-methylbutane with ⁻OH as base.

H and Br are anti to each other

base

Details: **1.** H – OH bond formed
2. C-H bond breaks
3. C=C double bond forms
4. C-Br bond breaks
(transition state shows **all of this at once**)

258

E1 mechanism of dehydrohalogenation

2 steps
Forms carbocation intermediate like S_N1 (3° (and some 2°) alkyl halides with weak base)
No need for anti-arrangement of halogen and adjacent H as in E2
1st order, unimolecular, rate = k[alkyl halide]

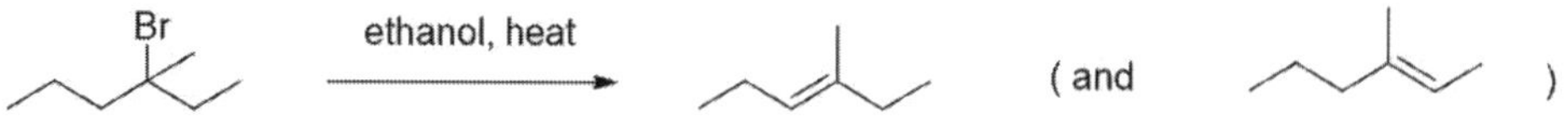

(be able to show a mechanism for formation of each product, transition states, RXN coordinate diagram)

259

E1 MECHANISM and reaction coordinate diagram (like S_N1)
another example or continue work from previous page

260

Leaving Groups for E1 and S_N1

Good leaving groups are

- conjugate bases of strong acids
- weak bases
- stable

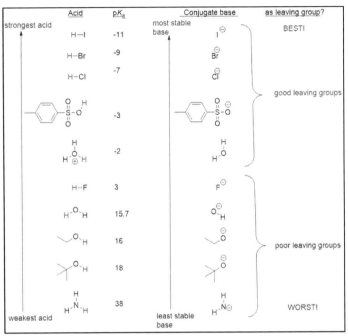

For E1 and S_N1, the first step (carbocation formation) is the slow rate determining step in these two-step reactions. So, the more stable the halide ion (leaving group) the faster the ionization.

The better the leaving group, the faster the S_N1 or E1 reaction.

Substrate in first order reaction, E1 and S_N1...carbocation stability

The **more stable the carbocation intermediate**, the **faster** the S_N1 or E1 reaction.

Solvolysis (solvent acts as reagent) reactions of **1° and 2° substrates** are slow/carbocation intermediates unstable. Don't expect first order product to be major product.

3° benzylic and allylic halides substrates have more stable carbocation intermediates. They can produce a mix of S_N1 and E1 products.

Mixture of products for 1st order substitution and elimination

solvolysis (reaction where the solvent is a reactant) to give a *mixture* of S_N1 and E1 products

Practice writing out each mechanism to justify formation of each product.

Practice: mixture of products for first order reactions (solvolysis again)

Can you work out the three possible products?

$$\text{2-chloro-2-methylbutane} \xrightarrow{\text{H}_2\text{O, heat}}$$

Be able to write out the mechanisms to show how each product is formed.

More practice E1 regioselectivity

Can you figure out the FOUR possible products for this one?

3-bromo-3-methylpentane $\xrightarrow{\text{H}_2\text{O, heat}}$

Why is (E)-3-methyl-2-pentene the major product?

Practice: name all products

Be able to write out the mechanisms to show how each product is formed.

Review of 1st and 2nd order substitution and elimination

S_N1	E1	vs	E2	S_N2

1st order
2 steps
Unimolecular slow step
Rate = k[R-LG]
  (independent of [**nuc**])
RXN coord diagram: 2 humps
3° (and 2°) substrates
Forms carbocation intermediate
    C+ rearrangement possible
	1st order
	2 steps
	Unimolecular slow step
	Rate = k[R-LG]
	  (independent of [**BASE**])
	RXN coord diagram: 2 humps
	3° substrates
	Forms carbocation intermediate
	    C+ rearrangement possible
			2nd order
			1 step (concerted)
			Bimolecular slow step
			Rate = k[R-LG][**BASE**]
			
			RXN coord diagram: 1 hump
			(concerted reaction)
			1° or 2° or 3° substrates
			NO carbocation formed
				2nd order
				1 step (concerted)
				Bimolecular slow step
				Rate = k[R-LG][**nuc**]
				
				RXN coord diagram: 1 hump
				(concerted reaction)
				Methyl, 1° or 2° substrates
				NO carbocation intermediate

Stereochemical outcome:
  ~50:50 mix (**racemic**)
 	
Polar protic solvents like water, MeOH, etc.
	Stereochemical outcome:
	  E over Z
	
	Regiochemical outcomes:
	  Zaitsev or Hofmann
			Stereochemical outcome:
			  Dependent on **antiperiplanar**
			    orientation of H and LG
			Regiochemical outcomes:
			  Zaitsev or Hofmann
				Stereochemical outcome:
				  inversion at electrophilic carbon
				
				Polar aprotic solvents like DMF, DMSO, CH$_3$CN, acetone, etc.

Product of E1 and E2 eliminations: **alkene**

Substitution S$_N$1, S$_N$2
vs
Elimination E1, E2

Substitution *vs* Elimination on **ALKYL HALIDE**:
Now it gets tricky

Both substitution and elimination reactions can occur on **alkyl halide RX**.
Is the base a base or a nucleophile?
Is the nucleophile a nucleophile or a base?

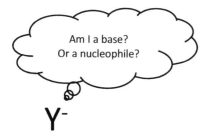

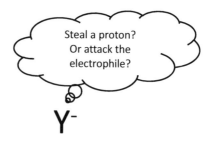

Substitution *vs* Elimination on Alkyl Halide

As we saw in solvolysis for first order reaction, both substitution and elimination reactions can occur on alkyl halide RX.

Is the base a base or a nucleophile?

Is the nucleophile a nucleophile or a base?

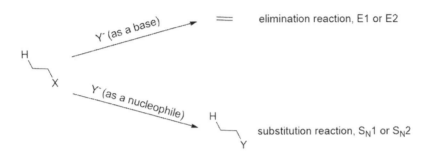

Y⁻ (as a base) → elimination reaction, E1 or E2

Y⁻ (as a nucleophile) → substitution reaction, S$_N$1 or S$_N$2

Substitution *vs* Elimination:

a guide for analysis of **substrate** and **reagents** to determine mechanism leading to major product

substrate	reagents Water, alcohol (solvolysis)	reagents Good nucleophile*	reagents Strong base**	reagents Bulky base (like *t*-butoxide)
Methyl X				
1° RX				
2° RX				
3° RX				

*good nuc: pK_a of conjugate acid<11
**good base: pK_a of conjugate acid >11

practice: Predicting products

Substrate alkyl halide: MeBr with

a. *t*-butoxide

b. ethoxide

c. hydrogen sulfide (HS⁻)

271

More practice: Predicting products

Substrate alkyl halide: 1-bromopropane with

a. Azide

b. Amide ($^-NH_2$)

c. *t*-butoxide

272

More practice: Predicting products

Substrate alkyl halide: Bromocyclohexane with

a. *t*-butoxide

b. Hydroxide

c. Sodium cyanide in DMSO

d. ethanol

More practice: Predicting products

Substrate alkyl halide: 2-bromo-2,3-dimethylpentane with

a. *t*-butoxide

b. water

practice

1. Choose the product which is *least likely to form* when 2S-chloropentane reacts with sodium ethoxide (NaOEt).

2. Choose the *major isolated organic product* from the reaction in question 1.

Answer choices for both questions:

A.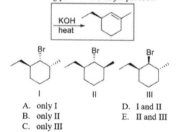

B.

C.

D.

E.

Practice

1. For the circled carbon in the Fischer projection of D-glucose, what are the Cahn-Ingold-Prelog priorities for the groups pointing up and down?

CHO
H——OH
HO——H
H——OH
H——OH
CH₂OH

A. Up: 1, Down: 2   C. Up: 2, Down: 3
B. Up: 2, Down: 1   D. Up: 3, Down: 2
E. None of the above

2. Which of the following molecules is an *enantiomer* for (1R,2S)-1-bromo-2-isopropyl cyclohexane?

A   B   C   D

3. Which of the following alkyl halides will give the following product as a major product?

KOH / heat

I   II   III

A. only I   D. I and II
B. only II   E. II and III
C. only III

Practice

4. Which of the following choices is a diastereomer of the first structure shown?

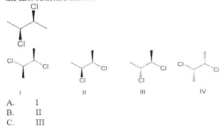

    I   II   III   IV

A. I
B. II
C. III
D. IV

5. In each pair given, which carbocation is more stable?

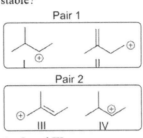

A. I and III
B. I and IV
C. II and III
D. II and IV

Practice

6. Which of the following alkyl halides will give the following product as a major product?

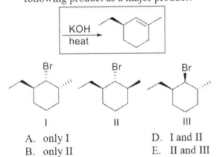

    I   II   III

A. only I   D. I and II
B. only II   E. II and III
C. only III

New substrate: alcohols

Alcohol as substrate for elimination or substitution

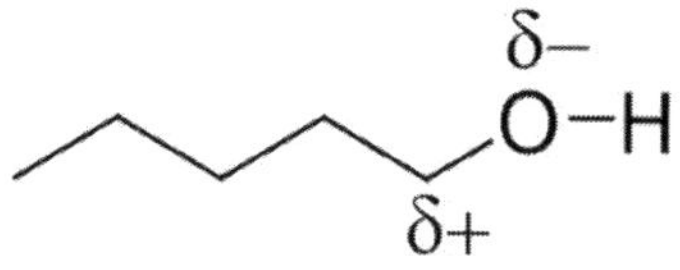

$\delta-$
O–H   alcohol
$\delta+$

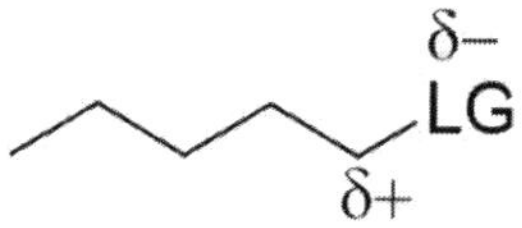

$\delta-$
LG
$\delta+$

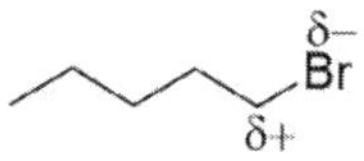

$\delta-$
Br   alkyl halide
$\delta+$

⁻OH is not a good leaving group.

Must **modify** it to make it a better leaving group.

Convert to water—better leaving group

Substitution reactions on alcohols

With HX to make alkyl halide

May be 1st or 2nd order depending on substrate

OH is bad leaving group. Must protonate it first.

Example with 1° alcohol: mechanism after protonation is S_N2

$$\text{CH}_3\text{CH}_2\text{CH}_2\text{CH}_2\text{O-H} \xrightarrow{\text{H-Br}} \text{CH}_3\text{CH}_2\text{CH}_2\text{CH}_2\text{Br} \quad (+ H_2O)$$

(2° or 3° alcohols generally follow S_N1 mechanism)

PRACTICE MECHANISM for conversion of tertiary alcohol to alkyl halide

For this reaction:

$$\underset{\substack{\text{OH} \\ \text{alcohol} \\ \text{2-methyl-2-propanol}}}{} \xrightarrow[25°C]{\text{HCl}} \underset{\substack{\text{Cl} \\ \text{alkyl halide} \\ \text{2-chloro-2-methylpropane}}}{} + H_2O$$

The mechanism is 3 steps:

protonation, elimination of water, nucleophilic attack.

(Classify as S_N1 or S_N2)

Practice: Alcohol with HBr, S_N1, carbocation rearrangement

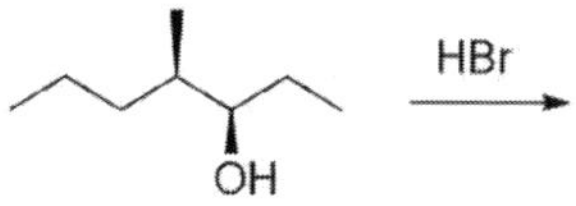

HBr

?????   (4-bromo-4-methylheptane!)

HOW did this happen??? S_N1 MECHANISM

4R-methyl-3R-heptanol

Elimination reactions on alcohols

"acid catalyzed dehydration"

Produces alkene

Requires concentrated sulfuric acid and heat

Alcohols (acid catalyzed dehydration) to alkenes

Alcohols will undergo **E1** elimination when reacted with H_2SO_4

The strongly acidic conditions are *protic* conditions, which favors E1 for 2° and 3° substrates. Write out mechanism.

8-285

E1 dehydration carbocation rearrangement: another example

Upon acid-catalyzed dehydration of 3,3-dimethyl-2-butanol, 2,3-dimethyl-2-butene is formed—instead of the expected product 3,3-dimethyl-1-butene.

Why? (think about carbocation rearrangement in mechanism in first order reactions)

286

Laura Lanni

143

Practice: E1 dehydration

Show why 2,2-dimethylcyclohexanol dehydrated with sulfuric acid makes 1,2-dimethylcyclohexene by writing the E1 mechanism.

PRACTICE
alcohol dehydration

What (name/structure) alkene is formed upon dehydration of each?

1. 3-ethyl-3-pentanol

2. 2-propanol

3. 1-propanol

4. 2,3,3-trimethyl-2-butanol

practice

Draw BOTH possible products of the dehydration of **1-methylcyclohexanol**, and circle the MAJOR product based on Zaitsev's rule.

289

practice

Draw and name the THREE alkene isomers *that could be* formed from the acid-catalyzed dehydration of 2-hexanol.

290

Laura Lanni

145

Recap: When reactant substrate is an alcohol (R-OH)

With HX: **substitution** (makes alkyl halide)

With heat and concentrated H_2SO_4: **elimination** (makes alkene)
        acid-catalyzed dehydration,
        make Zaitsev major product, E over Z

Note: By the end of this course, you will need to remember about 30 sets of reagents and how they convert one functional group to another. At the end of orgo 2, there will be almost 100 reactions to remember. Develop you best way to organize the reactions. Practice mechanisms. Make notecards with substrate/reagent/product by functional group, examples.

291

Addition reactions

292

Addition Reactions of Alkenes

Hydrogenation
    Stereochem: *syn* addition
Electrophilic addition of HX
    regioselectivity: Markovnikov
    mechanism, carbocation rearrangements
Acid catalyzed hydration
    Mechanism
    Markovnikov
Oxymercuration-demercuration
Hydroboration-oxidation
    Anti-Markovnikov, mechanism, stereochem
Addition of X_2
    mechanism
Halohydrin formation (mechanism)
Epoxidation (mechanism)
Oxidation to vicinal diol with OsO_4 (mechanism)
Ozonolysis (mechanism)
Multistep problem solving and retrosynthesis examples

293

General addition reaction to alkene

unsaturated	saturated
hydrocarbon	hydrocarbon
(alkene)	(alkane)

These reactions are called **electrophilic additions**.
In the first (slow) step, the nucleophilic electron-rich π bond attacks the electron-deficient "electrophile" on A-B. This makes a bond between one of the carbons of the double bond, and often leaves a carbocation on the other carbon (that just lost its π bond, and now only has three bonds).
The other half of AB, lurking in the reaction mix and now likely carrying a full negative charge, then rapidly attacks the carbocation in the second step.

294

General addition reaction to alkene

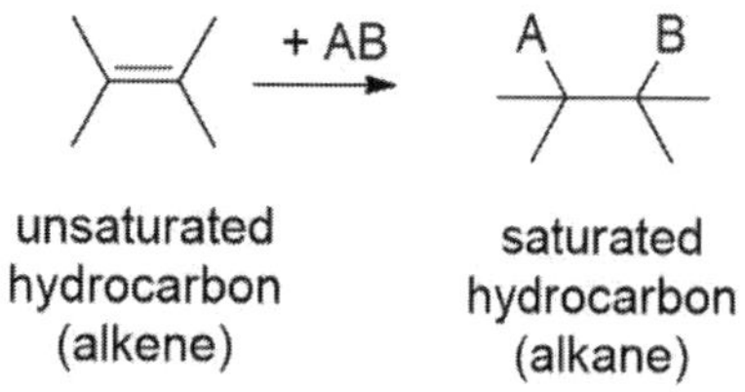

+ AB
A
B
unsaturated hydrocarbon (alkene)
saturated hydrocarbon (alkane)

Note that addition reactions are the reverse of *elimination* reactions.

Hydration	vs	*dehydration*
Hydrohalogenations	vs	*dehydrohalogenation*

295

Hydrogenation (reduce alkene to alkane)

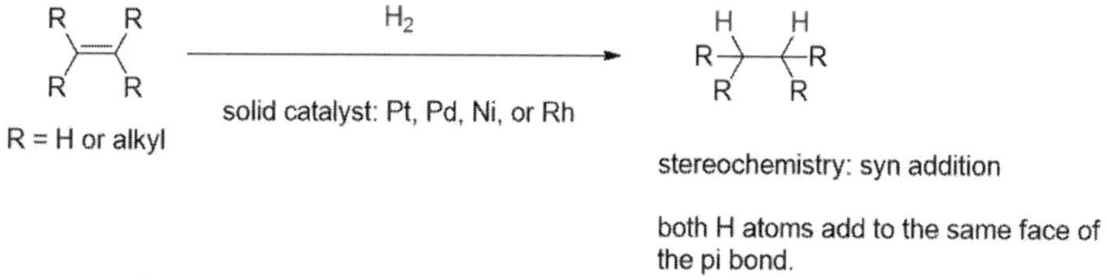

R
R
R
R
R = H or alkyl
H2
solid catalyst: Pt, Pd, Ni, or Rh
H
H
R
R
R
R
stereochemistry: syn addition
both H atoms add to the same face of the pi bond.

296

Hydrogenation example showing **syn addition** of H_2

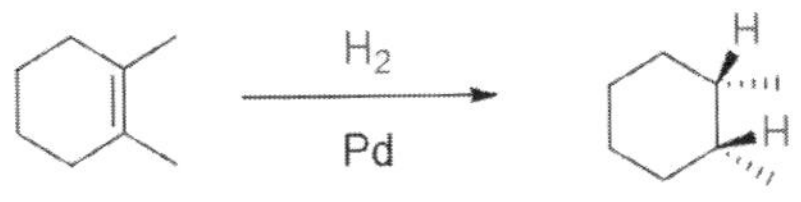

(the two methyls are *cis* to each other)
(the two hydrogens are *cis* to each other)

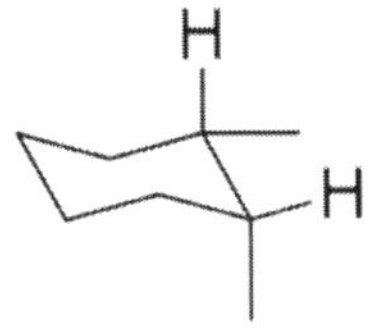

297

Electrophilic addition of hydrogen halides to alkenes: **hydrohalogenation**

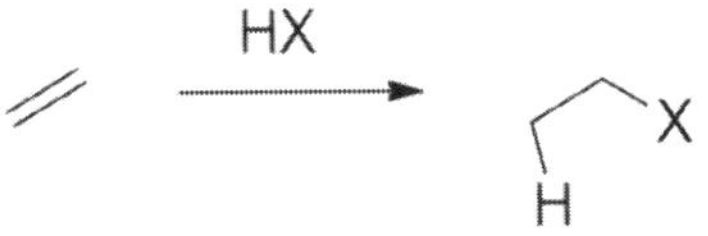

makes alkyl halide

example

2-butene

HBr

2-bromobutane

298

Regioselectivity of hydrohalogenation: Markovnikov's Rule

H will add to C of double bond with more Hs

(Then Br⁻ will add to MORE substituted C)

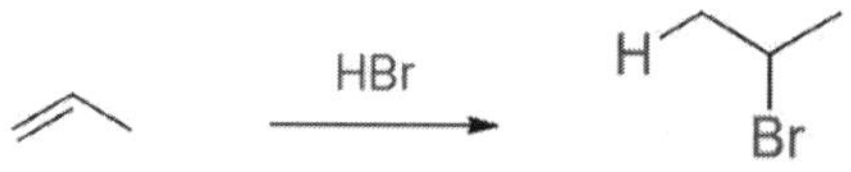

2-bromopropane

NOT

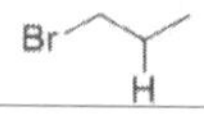

1-bromopropane

PRACTICE: Markovnikov's Rule

What is the structure and name of the major product after HCl is added to each?

1. 2-methyl-2-butene

2. 2-methyl-1-butene

3. cis-2-butene (*cis* means Z)

4.

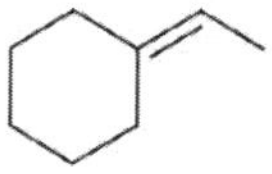

MECHANISM of alkene + HX (hydrohalogenation)

Example

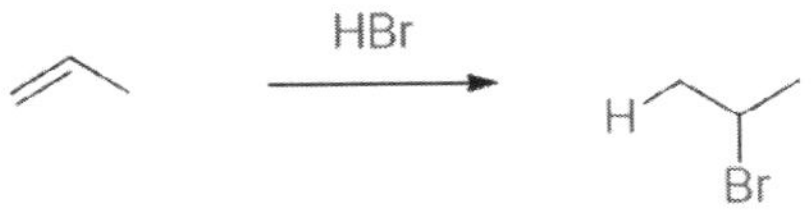

HBr

2-bromopropane

MECHANISM of alkene + HX

Why didn't HBr add the other way?

(*via* a mechanistic investigation we can see **carbocation stability** results in Markovnikov addition stereoselectivity)

Example/practice

What is the structure of the carbocation intermediate formed **after the first mechanistic step** of the reaction between 2-methyl-2-butene and HBr?

303

beware carbocation rearrangements for alkene + HX

example(s)

1. 3,3-dimethyl-1-butene + HCl yields 2-chloro-2,3-dimethylbutane (and not 2,2-dimethyl-3-chlorobutane)

2. 3R-methylcyclopentene + HCl yields 1-chloro-1-methylcyclopentane (justify by writing mechanism)

3. Must consider stereochemistry of product: HBr + 3-methyl-3-hexene

304

Add water to alkene to make alcohol (3 hydrations)

Acid catalyzed hydration

Oxymercuration-demercuration

Hydroboration-oxidation

acid-catalyzed HYDRATION: (add H-OH) to alkenes (to make alcohol)

Example

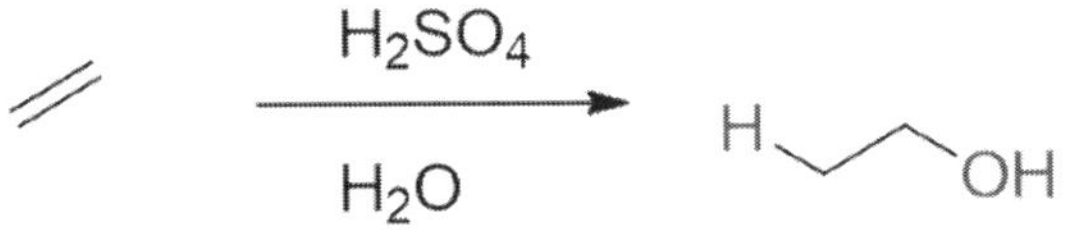

$$\xrightarrow[\text{H}_2\text{O}]{\text{H}_2\text{SO}_4}$$

(Note: H_2SO_4 and H_2O may be written as "dilute H_2SO_4", or "H_2SO_4(aq)", or "H_3O^+")
Regioselective—follows Markovnikov's Rule when applicable
Mechanism
Examples

acid-catalyzed hydration (add H-OH) to alkenes (to make alcohol)

Beware carbocation rearrangement

example

Oxymercuration/reduction (demercuration) (two steps to an alcohol)

In the oxymercuration step (step 1), water and mercuric acetate add to the double bond.

In the demercuration step (step 2), sodium borohydride reduces the acetomercury group and replaces it with a hydrogen.

The net addition of H and OH occurs with Markovnikov regioselectivity,

without carbocation rearrangement.

1. $Hg(OAc)_2$, H_2O
2. $NaBH_4$

Laura Lanni

hydroboration-oxidation of alkenes (two steps to an alcohol, another way)

Example

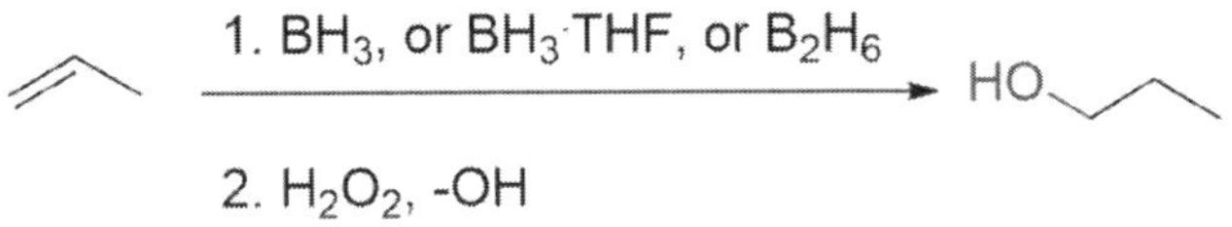

$$\text{(alkene)} \xrightarrow[\text{2. } H_2O_2, \text{ -OH}]{\text{1. } BH_3, \text{ or } BH_3 \cdot THF, \text{ or } B_2H_6} HO\text{(alcohol)}$$

Regioselective—**anti-Markovnikov**

Stereoselectivity—**syn addition** of H, OH across double bond

More examples

309

hydroboration-oxidation of alkenes: MECHANISM

310

hydroboration-oxidation of alkenes: more examples/ comparison to acid catalyzed hydration

When propene is hydrated by each of the three sets of reagents, what alcohol products are formed in each case?

_____

When 3-methyl-1-pentene is hydrated by each of the three sets of reagents, a different alcohol product is formed in each case. What are they?

311

Addition of halogens to alkenes

Examples and mechanism

$\begin{array}{c} = \end{array}$ $\xrightarrow[\text{(X}_2)]{\text{Br}_2}$ Br   Br

vicinal dibromide

anti addition (stereoselective)

312

practice

Write the full mechanism, including appropriate and specific arrow pushing to show the flow of electrons, being careful of formal charges and start and end points of each arrow, and indicating the correct product(s) for each reaction:

1. 1-pentene + HBr

2. 1-pentene + aqueous sulfuric acid

313

Conversion of alkenes to vicinal halohydrins

$$\overset{Br_2}{\underset{H_2O}{\longrightarrow}}$$ Br⟍___OH   anti addition (stereoselective)

halohydrin   regioselectivity: OH will be on MORE substituted C of product

mechanism, example, practice

314

Epoxidation of alkenes using peroxyacid (like mcpba)

Alkene and *meta*-chloroperoxybenzoic acid (mcpba)

$$\diagup\diagup \xrightarrow{\quad RCO_3H \quad} \triangle$$

$$\diagup\diagup \xrightarrow{\quad mcpba \quad} \triangle$$

epoxide

Mechanism

Ozonolysis of alkenes

Oxidative cleavage

$$R_1R\text{-}C=C\text{-}R_2R_3 \xrightarrow[\text{2. } (CH_3)_2S]{\text{1. } O_3} R(R_1)C=O \quad O=C(R_3)R_2$$

ketones and aldehydes produced

$(CH_3)_2S$ is dimethylsulfide (DMS)
ALTERNATIVE REDUCING AGENT: Zn/H_2O

Examples

Make **vicinal diol** (dihydroxylation)

Mechanism of first step shows *syn* addition.

Alternative reagent: $KMnO_4$, NaOH, cold

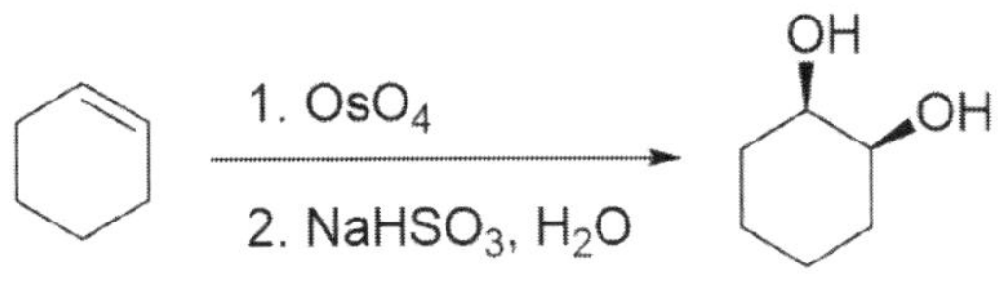

1. OsO_4

2. $NaHSO_3$, H_2O

317

Anti-Markovnikov hydrohalogenation: alkene + HX with peroxide

Mechanism later in the semester—a radical reaction, mechanism uses homolytic arrows.

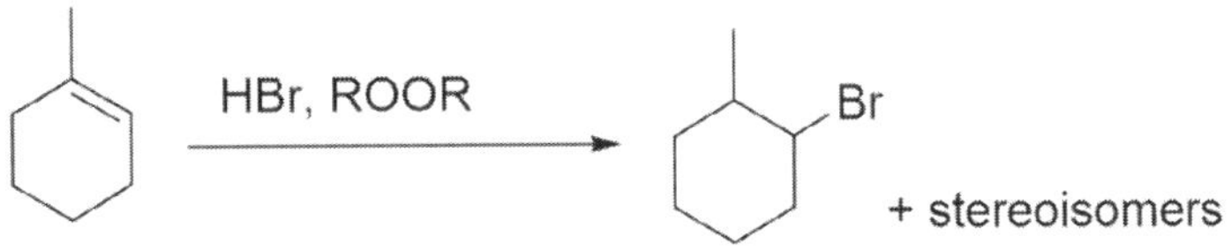

HBr, ROOR

Br

+ stereoisomers

318

Reactions of alkenes	Product
Hydrogenation *stereochem: syn addition*	alkane
Electrophilic addition of HX "hydrohalogenation"	alkyl halide RX
— regioselectivity: Markovnikov	
— mechanism, carbocation rearrangements	
Electrophilic addition of HX "hydrohalogenation" with peroxide	alkyl halide RX
Anti-Markovnikov	
Acid catalyzed hydration mechanism, C^+ rearrangement	alcohol ROH
— Markovnikov	
Oxymercuration-demercuration Markovnikov	alcohol ROH
Hydroboration-oxidation	alcohol ROH
— Anti-Markovnikov, mechanism, *stereochem (syn)*	
Addition of X_2 mechanism, *stereochem (anti)*	vicinal dihalide RX_2
Halohydrin formation mechanism, *stereochem (anti),* regiochem	halohydrin ROHX
Epoxidation mechanism	epoxide
Oxidation with OsO_4 mechanism, *stereochem*	vicinal diol $R(OH)_2$
Ozonolysis mechanism	ketones, aldehydes (C=O)

319

Multistep reactions

String together a series of organic reactions to produce a desired product from a given starting material.

Example: 3-methyl-2-pentanol undergoes this series of steps.
1. $SOCl_2$, pyridine (converts alcohol to alkyl chloride)
2. Potassium *t*-butoxide
3. H_2, Pd

Be able to draw the product after each step to show that the final product is 3-methylpentane.

more examples

320

Multistep reactions

More examples

2-ethylcyclohexanol $\xrightarrow[\begin{array}{l}\text{2. NaOMe}\\\text{3. }H_2SO_4\text{, }H_2O\end{array}]{\text{1. }PBr_3\text{, pyridine}}$

(note: PBr_3, pyridine is interchangeable here with HBr)

321

Multistep reactions

More examples

$\xrightarrow{\text{methoxide}}$ $\xrightarrow{Br_2}$

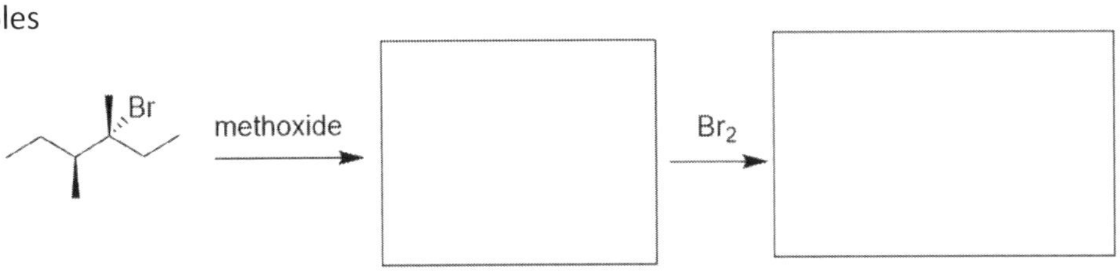

(Hint: need Newman Projection for first reaction.)

322

Multistep reactions

More examples

2-chloropropane →
1. potassium t-butoxide
2. mcpba

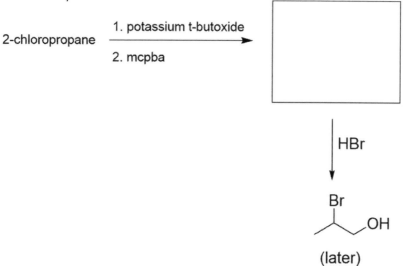

↓ HBr

Br
|
/\/OH

(later)

Multistep reactions

More examples

2-methyl-2-butanol →
1. concentrated sulfuric acid
2. B_2H_6
3. hydrogen peroxide and sodium hydroxide

Multistep reactions

More examples

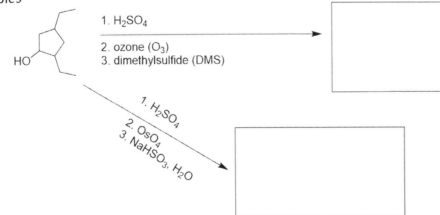

1. H_2SO_4

2. ozone (O_3)
3. dimethylsulfide (DMS)

Multistep reactions

More examples

1. H_2SO_4

2. ozone (O_3)
3. dimethylsulfide (DMS)

1. H_2SO_4
2. OsO_4
3. $NaHSO_3$, H_2O

More examples?

ALKYNES

Laura Lanni

Alkynes

Nomenclature

Properties

Structure/bonding, sp hybridization

Acidity of acetylene and terminal alkynes

Preparation by alkylation of acetylene and terminal alkynes

Preparation by elimination RXNs

RXNs of alkynes: hydrogenation, Lindlar, metal-ammonia reduction, add RX, hydration—
Mark and anti-Mark, add HX or X_2 (1 eq or 2 equiv)

Multistep syntheses, retrosynthesis

Alkyne nomenclature

C_nH_{2n-2}

Triple bond between two sp hybridized carbons

Use organic prefixes with –yne suffix

Laura Lanni

Alkyne nomenclature/ hybridization

closest to either multiple bond

1-octen-4-yne

REVIEW CONCEPTS: Indicate hybridization of each carbon and describe each carbon-carbon bond

Carbon-carbon bond comparison (general chemistry review)

	C≡C		C=C		C–C
length:	triple bond	<	double bond	<	single bond
strength:	triple bond	>	double bond	>	single bond

Triple bond is shortest and strongest

Laura Lanni

Terminal alkyne acidity

R─≡─H

pKa = 25
on sp C

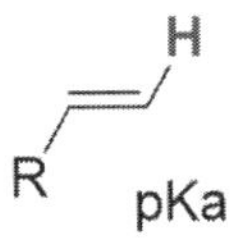

pKa = 40
on sp^2 C

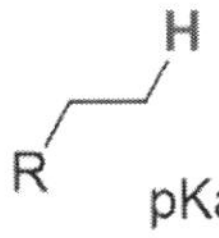

pKa = 50-60
on sp^3 C

333

Deprotonate **terminal alkyne**

Use base called amide $^-NH_2$
(sodium amide: **NaNH$_2$**)
(sodium hydride works too: **NaH**)
(in both bases, the sodium is a *spectator ion*)

Example: **1-pentyne + sodium amide...**
(product = carbanion, a carbon nucleophile)

334

Carbanion nucleophile reacts with 1° alkyl halide (S_N2)

Makes new C-C bond   Makes **longer alkyne**

Example: Acetylene to 2-hexyne (in many steps)
     (be careful to count carbons)

Prepare alkynes by elimination

Double dehydrohalogenation of vicinal (or geminal) dihalide

Reagents: 1. 3 equivalents ("xs") $NaNH_2$

              2. water

(Note, second water step needed for terminal alkyne.)

Example: 1,2-dibromobutane to 1-butyne

     AND mechanism (Eliminate, eliminate, deprotonate, protonate)

Laura Lanni

Prepare alkynes by elimination

Another example (FITB style):

ethene to "more-than-2-carbon-alkyne" in ~5 steps

practice

Design a series of synthetic steps to make **2,2,-dimethyl-4-octyne** starting from 1-pentene

Laura Lanni

Reactions of alkynes: HYDROGENATION (reduction)

Hydrogenation (3 RXNs) can make **ALKANES** or **ALKENES**

Examples (no mechanisms)

2-pentyne to pentane

2-pentyne to Z-2-pentene

2-pentyne to E-2-pentene

339

Reactions of alkynes: **HYDRATION**

Hydration: add water across triple bond (makes unstable enol)

Can be Markovnikov or anti-Markovnikov

Keto-enol **tautomerization (NEW!)**

Products are **ketones** (Mark)

           or **aldehydes** (anti-Mark)

Examples (including the Markovnikov mechanism, with tautomerization)

340

Reactions of alkynes: **HYDRATION**

Examples (including the Markovnikov mechanism, with tautomerization, makes KETONE)

Just structures

1. propyne $\xrightarrow{\text{H}_2\text{O, H}_2\text{SO}_4\text{, Hg(OAC)}_2}$ propanone (acetone)

Add mechanism

2. 1-pentyne $\xrightarrow{\text{H}_2\text{O, H}_2\text{SO}_4\text{, Hg(OAC)}_2}$ 2-pentanone

341

Reactions of alkynes: **HYDRATION**

Example (Anti-Markovnikov hydration, makes aldehyde on terminal alkyne) (no mechanism)

1-pentyne $\xrightarrow{\text{1. R}_2\text{BH} \quad \text{2. H}_2\text{O}_2\text{, }^-\text{OH}}$ pentanal (an aldehyde)

(Note: R_2BH is a bulky borane, like $(sia)_2BH$, or 9-BBN)

342

Questions, concerns, misconceptions, multistep examples, make more notecards?

Reactions of alkynes: Hydrohalogenation Add one or two equivalents of **HX to alkyne**

One equivalent HX makes **Markovnikov alkene**

TWO equivalents HX makes **geminal dibromide** (alkane)

Examples (easy mechanism)

344

Laura Lanni

Reactions of alkynes: **HALOGENATION**

Halogenation, consider molar ratio: add X_2

1 equivalent X_2 makes dihalo-alkene
2 equivalents X_2 makes tetrahaloalkane

Example

practice: Alkyne review: how to make and do all of the reactions on 1-butyne

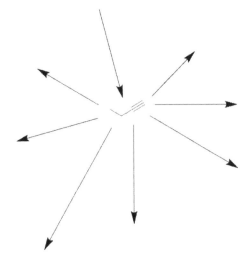

Laura Lanni

Practice synthesis

Design a series of steps to make 4-octanol from acetylene

Practice synthesis

Design a series of steps to make starting from acetylene

Practice: Propose a mechanism which justifies each product

1.

bromine

water

Br

ΙΙΟΗ

Br

OH

2.

sulfuric acid

methanol

O

349

Practice: Propose a mechanism which justifies each product

3.

HO

HI

I

4.

aqueous sulfuric acid

OH

350

Practice: Multistep synthetic design

Design a synthetic series of steps to produce butanone, 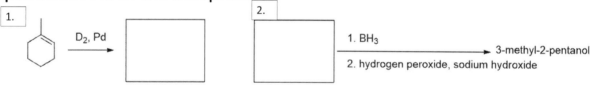 , from 2-propanol.

practice: Fill in the box practice

1.

D_2, Pd →

2.

1. BH_3

2. hydrogen peroxide, sodium hydroxide

→ 3-methyl-2-pentanol

3.

1. ozone

2. dimethyl sulfide

→

4.

1. ozone

2. dimethyl sulfide

→

352

Laura Lanni

176

practice

Draw the final major isolated organic product(s) of this series of reactions?

3-methyl-1-butene

1. Br$_2$
2. NaNH$_2$ (excess)
3. 9-BBN
4. H$_2$O$_2$, NaOH

353

Radical reactions

354

Laura Lanni

177

How to make RX (alkyl halide) from **alkanes**? (instead of alcohols or alkenes)

Alkanes are unreactive—they are nonpolar molecules which have no nucleophilic or electrophilic properties.

Therefore, reaction requires very high temperatures (400 °C, designated Δ) or energy supplied by UV light which are photochemical reactions (designated by hν)

Reaction occurs *via* a radical mechanism.

355

How to make RX from alkanes? (instead of alcohols)

Radical? A species with an unpaired electron

How are radicals formed? Homolytic cleavage

Normal (heterolytic) mechanism arrows show movement of a pair of electrons and use normal arrow head.

Homolytic cleavage is designated by a single headed arrow moving a single electron.

356

Radical mechanism steps

Simplified definitions

1. Initiation (formation of a radical)
2. Propagation (radical makes another radical)
3. Termination (2 radicals combine)

Example and mechanism...

Note: regioselectivity 2° over 1° consistently due to radical stability. More complicated when compare 1° to 3°. 357

Radical stability trend

Same order as carbocation stability trend (due to hyperconjugation)

| methyl | 1° | 2° | 3° | allylic and benzylic |

Least stable...most stable

allylic and benzylic
stabilized by resonance

358

Regioselectivity (1° vs 2°) between chlorination and bromination

In hydrogen abstraction propagation step, developing radical is more stable on 2° than 1° carbon

Bromination is much slower than chlorination, so it is more selective.

Difference in regioselectivity (1° vs 3°) between chlorination and bromination

Difference due to energy of transition state during hydrogen abstraction (propagation) step.

Bromination is more selective for the lower energy pathway.

Free radical addition of hydrogen bromide to alkenes (review, but add mechanism now)

(Review) In the presence of peroxide, this is a radical mechanism and forms the **anti-Markovnikov** product.

anti-Mark addition of HBr across double bond

(New) Mechanism, examples, compare to HBr addition with no peroxide?

361

plastics

Bottles, bags, toys, pens and pencils, laptop casing, model kit, Ziploc bags, cups, clearcoat on your car...plastics are addition polymers

(next semester: condensation polymers...polyester, polypeptides, nylon...)

362

Laura Lanni

Alkene polymerization

Addition polymers are made from alkene **MONO**mers

The carbon-carbon double bond is called a **vinyl group**.

A chain reaction of vinyl (alkene) monomers makes addition polymers, like polyethylene, polypropylene, polystyrene, polyvinylchloride (PVC), Teflon, and more.

363

Alkene Polymerization

(Cationic or) *radical* reaction

$$n \quad \overset{R}{=} \quad \xrightarrow[\text{or hv}]{H_2SO_4} \quad \cdots \overset{R}{\diagup}\overset{R}{\diagup}\overset{R}{\diagup}\overset{R}{\diagup}\overset{R}{\diagup}\overset{R}{\diagup} \cdots$$

monomer   polymer

364

Polyethylene from ethylene

Polypropylene from propene

Polystyrene from styrene

Polyvinyl chloride (PVC) from vinyl chloride

PRACTICE: Draw the polymer which would be formed from 1,1,2,2-tetrafluoroethene

Indicate the repeating unit.

Guess the trade name.

Ideas about uses?

369

Practice: what monomer made this polymer?

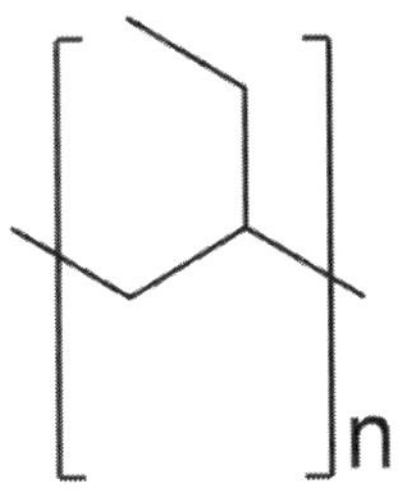

370

Recap: orgo 1 reactions (so far)

Substitutions

Eliminations

Additions to alkenes

Oxidations

Additions to alkynes

Radical reactions

Reagents which may be useful, if you know what they do.

NaOMe	NaNH$_2$ (or NaH)
KOtBu or KOC(CH$_3$)$_3$	NaNH$_2$ (excess)
1. TsCl, pyridine 2. nucleophile	1. NaNH$_2$ (3 eq) 2. H$_2$O
HBr	H$_2$, Pt (or Pd)
H$_2$SO$_4$ (concentrated, sometimes shown with heat or Δ)	H$_2$, Lindlar
H$_2$, Pt (or Pd)	Na, NH$_3$
X$_2$ like Br$_2$	HgSO$_4$, H$_2$SO$_4$, H$_2$O
Br$_2$, H$_2$O	1. R$_2$BH (like (sia)$_2$BH or 9-BBN) 2. H$_2$O$_2$, NaOH
H$_2$SO$_4$, H$_2$O	HBr (1 eq)
HBr	HBr (excess, or 2 eq)
1. Hg(OAc)$_2$ 2. NaBH$_4$	Br$_2$ (1 eq)
1. BH$_3$ 2. H$_2$O$_2$, NaOH	Br$_2$ (excess, or 2 eq)
1. O$_3$ 2. DMS ((CH$_3$)$_2$S) (or Zn/H$_2$O)	Br$_2$, hv
1. OsO$_4$ 2. NaHSO$_4$, H$_2$O	HBr, ROOR
mcpba (or RCO$_3$H)	

371

reaction recap

372

PRACTICE: What is produced in 1, and what is the monomer for 2?

1.

HBr

ROOR

2.

R=methyl

PRACTICE

3.

In the addition reaction of Br_2 to an alkene, the pi (π) electrons of the alkene act(s) as a(n) _____ .

A. nucleophile
B. electrophile
C. free radical
D. A and B
E. A and C

4. Which is true about the reaction shown? (Note: the reactant is shown as a Fischer projection.)

A. the product will have S configuration
B. the product will have R configuration
C. the product will not have a stereocenter
D. racemization will occur

PRACTICE

5. What is the major product of the following reaction?

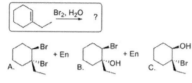

A. Br / ''Br + En

B. Br / ''OH + En

C. OH / ''Br + En

D. Br / ''OH + En

E. OH / ''Br + En

6. Which reactions can make only one product, and which can make a racemic mix?

I: 2-methyl-1-butene + Br_2
II: 2-methyl-1-butene + H_2 with solid platinum
III: 2-methyl-1-butene + 1. BH_3, 2. H_2O_2, NaOH

	One product	Racemic mix
A.	none	I, II, III
B.	I and III	II
C.	I	II and III
D.	II	I and III
E.	II and III	I

PRACTICE

7.

Which reagents will react with 3,3-dimethyl-1-octene to make these products?

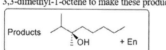

Products ... OH + En

A. 1. BH_3, 2. H_2O_2, ⁻OH
B. H_2SO_4, heat
C. H_2SO_4 (aq)
D. 1. H_2O, Hg(OAc)₂, 2. $NaBH_4$
E. More than one of these

8.

Recall the mechanisms for E1 acid-catalyzed dehydration and addition of bromine to determine the major isolated organic product(s) of these two successive reactions.

1. H_2SO_4, heat
2. Br_2

A. Br / Br + diast.

B. Br / Br + En

C. Br / Br + diast.

D. Br / Br + diast.

E. Br / Br + En

9.

How would you describe the stereochemistry of the product of the following reaction sequence?

1-butyne
1. NaH
2. Ethyl Iodide
3. Na, NH₃
4. Br_2

A. A pair of enantiomers
B. A pair of diastereomers
C. A pair of resonance structures
D. A pair of tautomers
E. A meso compound

Laura Lanni

ALCOHOLS, ETHERS, EPOXIDES

alcohols, ethers, epoxides (review and new)

ROH with PBr$_3$ or SOCl$_2$/pyridine

ROH with sulfonyl chloride→ Sulfonate ester

    Sulfonate ester + nuc: predict products

ROH Oxidation (and reduction)

Ether +HX (ether cleavage, makes RX and R'X)

Epoxide + nucleophiles (compare acidic and basic conditions)

Advice: Review sections of text before lecture. Then read them again after lecture.

Alcohol R-OH   Ether R-O-R'   Epoxide

Laura Lanni   189

alcohols

The **alcohol** functional group is not a good leaving group. Often, it will be "**activated**" (either protonated, or converted to halide, or made into sulfonate ester) prior to nucleophilic attack.

Be mindful of S_N2 reactions on chiral centers (inversion).
(**even number** of S_N2 steps **retains stereochemistry** of alcohol)

379

ROH with PBr$_3$ or SOCl$_2$/pyridine

Makes alkyl halide. Know both mechanisms.

Use PBr$_3$
(phosphorus tribromide)
(no mech required)

ROH $\xrightarrow{\text{PBr}_3}$ RX   Example:

Use SOCl$_2$
(thionyl chloride)
(KNOW mechanism)
useful for making
1° and 2° alkyl chlorides

ROH $\xrightarrow[\text{in pyridine}]{\text{SOCl}_2}$ RX   Example:

380

Laura Lanni

ROH with sulfonyl chloride makes sulfonate ester

Primary or secondary* alcohol can be converted to sulfonate ester—this **activates** it for further substitution, because the sulfonate ester is an excellent leaving group.

$$ROH \quad + \quad Cl-\underset{O}{\overset{O}{S}}-R' \quad \xrightarrow{\text{pyridine}} \quad RO-\underset{O}{\overset{O}{S}}-R' \quad (+ \; Cl^- \; \text{and pyridinium})$$

(S$_N$2)

(Three common examples ClSO$_2$R)

*If secondary alcohol is chiral...subsequent nucleophilic attack on sulfonate ester will produce inversion compared to original alcohol.

Sulfonate ester + nuc: predict products

$$\underset{R'}{O}-\underset{O}{\overset{O}{S}}-R' \quad + \quad nuc \quad \xrightarrow{S_N2} \quad R\text{-}nuc \quad + \quad \overset{\ominus}{O}-\underset{O}{\overset{O}{S}}-R'$$

Laura Lanni

Oxidation and reduction

Remember REDOX in general chemistry?

Oxidation and reduction in organic chemistry

Oxidation:
oxygen content increases and/or
hydrogen content decreases

Reduction:
oxygen content decreases and/or
hydrogen content increases

Laura Lanni

Oxidation examples by functional group

Alkene → alcohol

Alcohol → aldehyde or ketone

Aldehyde → carboxylic acid or ester

Alkane → alkene → alkyne

Oxidation reagents—for oxidation of alcohols (aka oxidizing agents)

H_2CrO_4 (chromic acid), Na_2CrO_4, $H_2Cr_2O_7$, $Na_2Cr_2O_7$

["Jones reagent" $CrO_3/Na_2Cr_2O_7$ in H_2SO_4(aq)]

PCC: pyridinium chlorochromate
     (see structure page 534)
          Made from CrO_3/HCl in pyridine

(HOCl (hypochlorous acid) via NaOCl with acetic acid, 0°C)

Laura Lanni   193

Oxidation considerations and examples

1° alcohol oxidation

2° alcohol oxidation

(cannot oxidize 3° alcohol. Why?)

Which reagent to use?

(and mechanism with HOCl)

387

Common Ethers (R-O-R')

.

388

Ether +HX (where X is I or Br)
"Ether cleavage"

S$_N$1 or S$_N$2 mechanisms (protonate, substitute, protonate, substitute)

$$\text{(CH}_3\text{)}_3\text{C}-\text{O}-\text{CH}_3 \xrightarrow[\text{(S}_N\text{2)}]{\text{H-I}} \xrightarrow[\text{(S}_N\text{1)}]{\text{H-I}} \text{(CH}_3\text{)}_3\text{C}-\text{I} \; + \; \text{H}_3\text{C}-\text{I}$$

389

Ether +HX   "Ether cleavage"

S$_N$1 or S$_N$2 mechanisms (protonate, substitute, protonate, substitute)

$$\text{CH}_3-\text{O}-\text{CH}_2\text{CH}_2\text{CH}_3 \xrightarrow[\text{(S}_N\text{2) (twice)}]{\text{H-Br (excess)}} \text{CH}_3\text{CH}_2\text{CH}_2-\text{Br} \; + \; \text{H}_3\text{C}-\text{Br}$$

390

Laura Lanni

195

Epoxide + nucleophiles

Epoxide + HX (or ROH) under **acidic conditions**, nucleophile will attack **MORE** substituted C in epoxide ring (for electronic reasons). In acid conditions... shows nuc attacks 1° over 2°, and nuc attacks 3° over 1° or 2°. In acid conditions, don't attack 2° carbon of epoxide (unless they're both 2°).

Epoxide + nuc (like alkoxide) under **neutral or basic conditions**, nucleophile will attack **LESS** substituted C in epoxide ring (for steric reasons).

Strong nucleophiles will attack the less substituted carbon of the epoxide due to sterics.

391

Epoxide + nucleophiles

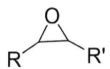

Epoxide + HX (or ROH) under acidic conditions

392

Epoxide + nucleophiles

Epoxide + nuc (like alkoxide) under basic conditions

More examples

Laura Lanni

practice   2-bromo-3-methylbutane $\xrightarrow{\ ?\ }$ 1-bromo-3-methylbutane

C. 1. NaOEt
   2. HBr

H 1. t-BuOK
   2. HBr

E. 1. NaOEt
   2. HBr, ROOR

J. 1. t-BuOK
    2. HBr, ROOR

Examples and practice

1. PBr₃ → 2. NaI

1. TsCl, pyridine → 2. NaBr

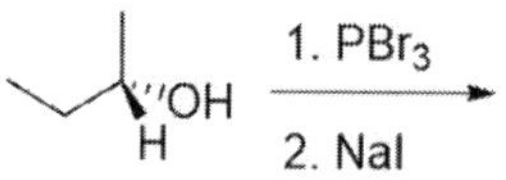

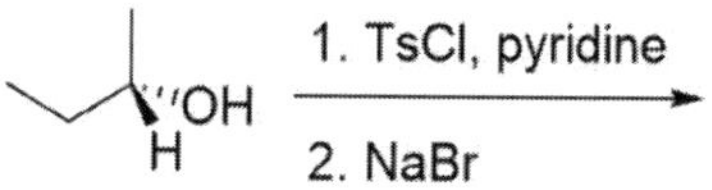

Propose a reaction mechanism to justify
formation of this product in this reaction.

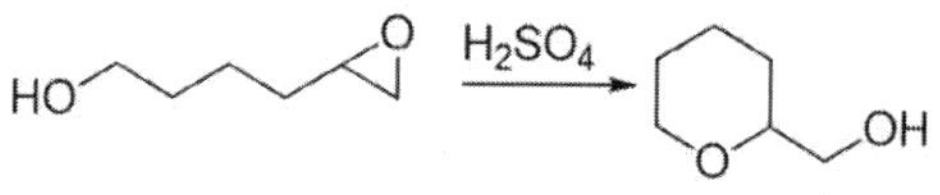

HO‒‒‒‒ (epoxide) $\xrightarrow{H_2SO_4}$ (tetrahydropyran)‒OH

Laura Lanni

198

orgo 1 Reagents

NaOMe	1. NaNH$_2$ (excess) 2. H$_2$O
KOtBu or KOC(CH$_3$)$_3$	H$_2$, Pt (or Pd)
1. TsCl, pyridine 2. nucleophile	H$_2$, Lindlar
HBr	Na, NH$_3$
H$_2$SO$_4$ (concentrated, sometimes shown with heat or Δ)	HgSO$_4$, H$_2$SO$_4$, H$_2$O
H$_2$, Pt (or Pd)	1. R$_2$BH (like (sia)$_2$BH or 9-BBN) 2. H$_2$O$_2$, NaOH
X$_2$ like Br$_2$	HBr (1 eq)
Br$_2$, H$_2$O	HBr (excess, or 2 eq)
H$_2$SO$_4$, H$_2$O	Br$_2$ (1 eq)
HBr	Br$_2$ (excess, or 2 eq)
1. Hg(OAc)$_2$ 2. NaBH$_4$	Br$_2$, hv
1. BH$_3$ 2. H$_2$O$_2$, NaOH	HBr, ROOR
1. O$_3$ 2. DMS ((CH$_3$)$_2$S) (or Zn/H$_2$O)	SOCl$_2$, pyridine
1. OsO$_4$ 2. NaHSO$_3$, H$_2$O	PBr$_3$ (or PCl$_3$)
mcpba (or RCO$_3$H)	H$_2$CrO$_4$ (Na$_2$CrO$_4$, Na$_2$Cr$_2$O$_7$, Jones, etc)
NaNH$_2$ (or NaH)	PCC (pyridinium chlorochromate)
NaNH$_2$ (excess)	NaOCl, CH$_3$COOH, 0°C

PRACTICE

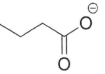

This ion is called butanoate and all of the formal charges are shown.

a. How many valence electrons are in this carboxylate?
b. Draw all lone pairs on the ion.
c. What is the shape around the carbon bonded to the oxygens?
d. What is the hybridization of that carbon?
e. What is the shape around all of the other carbons?
f. What is the hybridization of those carbons?
g. What is the formula for this particle?
h. Describe the double bond between the carbon and oxygen.
i. Draw a valid resonance structure.

j. Draw the conjugate acid.

k. Design a synthesis to produce the conjugate acid from ethane.

l. Write the mechanism for as many steps as you can in the synthesis you designed.

Laura Lanni

PRACTICE

a. What is the pKa of each proton?

b. Draw the conjugate base of each.

c. Which conjugate base is strongest?
d. Which conjugate base is weakest?
e. Which conjugate base is most stable?

399

PRACTICE

a. Give the IUPAC name of this molecule. _____

b. Formula: _____

c. How many **butane** constitutional isomers exist for this compound? _____

d. How many cycloalkane isomers exist for this compound? _____

e. Draw and give the IUPAC name of the *other* four (4) **pentane** isomers.

400

Laura Lanni

PRACTICE

a. What type(s) of intermolecular forces exist between molecules of hydrocarbons to hold them in the liquid or solid state?

b. What type(s) of intermolecular forces exist between molecules of alcohols to hold them in the liquid or solid state?

c. Which has the lowest boiling point? Why?

      hexane   2-methylpentane 2,2-dimethylbutane

d. Which has the highest boiling point? Why?

      Hexane   pentane butane

e. Why are hydrocarbons insoluble in water? Why?

f. What makes ethanol soluble in water?

401

PRACTICE

Name this molecule from its Newman projection

Draw a staggered Newman projection of 3-ethyl-2-methylhexane along the C_2-C_3 bond. (Did you draw the R or S isomer?)

402

Laura Lanni

PRACTICE

a. Name this molecule

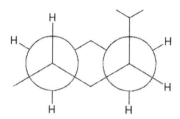

b. Are the alkyl branches *cis* or *trans* to one another?

c. Is the methyl group axial or equatorial?

d. What is its formula?

403

PRACTICE

Draw this tri-substituted cyclohexane on the chair per the pre-numbered carbons, and then draw the flipped chair. Do not rotate the chair.

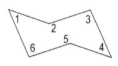 

404

Laura Lanni

Mechanism list

Even if you are not formally required to write out every mechanism for credit, the skill of arrow pushing to show bonds forming and breaking can lead you to the correct product structures on other types of questions.

405

orgo 1 Recap

406

Other questions?

407

408

Made in the USA
Middletown, DE
19 August 2021